Date Due

No. 490
$7.95

Advanced Techniques for
TROUBLESHOOTING WITH THE OSCILLOSCOPE

Robert L. Goodman

TAB BOOKS
BLUE RIDGE SUMMIT, PA. 17214

FIRST EDITION

FIRST PRINTING — FEBRUARY 1969

Copyright © 1968 by TAB BOOKS

Preface

I vividly remember a sign on a country road: "Choose your ruts carefully—you will be in them for the next twenty miles!" Let's hope that admonition doesn't apply to your career as an electronics technician. Instead, let us assume that you recognize the importance of keeping pace with technology and the demands rapid advances place on those of us who must keep electronic equipment working.

To some technicians the mere mention of a triggered-sweep scope conjures up big dollar signs and the image of a piece of equipment so complex and difficult to use that any thought of using one is abandoned. Those who still think this way are in the proverbial "rut." Today, a triggered sweep is almost a necessity! Moreover, as you will learn in this book, the use of this sophisticated instrument is not difficult. And recently-introduced triggered sweep scopes are now priced within the budget range of most shops.

We might as well face the fact that in the very near future much of our electronic service work will require a scope of this caliber. In fact, this book will show you how to simplify some of your present troubleshooting procedures! Many new fault-finding diagnoses are possible with the aid of the triggered scope and pulse or square-wave generator. The testing of ICs, RC multicomponent networks, molecularized and micromodules are just a few areas where such advanced procedures are necessary. And every day finds the introduction of more electronic IC units in the consumer products we must service. Actually, the professional triggered scope is about the only equipment you can use to troubleshoot ICs, unless you want to buy an expensive IC tester! So don't deprive yourself of the use of a triggered-sweep scope any longer. If you don't have one, it is hoped the information here will help you decide which one to buy. It is also hoped that the material in the book will help you develop the ability to put it to work.

I am particularly indebted to Tektronix, Inc., Beaverton, Oregon, for permission to use material from their oscilloscope manuals and scope circuitry handbooks, also for the use of a scope camera used to photograph the many oscillograms contained herein. In addition, I am grateful to Mr. Terrell Jamison and Mr. Del Bretzman, Field Engineers with Tektronix, Inc., Houston, Texas, for their assistance and cooperation, and to a host of electronic technical representatives and fellow electronic technicians whose comments have contributed enormously to information contained in this book. Thanks also to my wife, Jackie, who diligently typed and corrected the entire manuscript. Without her assistance this book would not have been possible.

Other companies who cooperated in furnishing material are:
Heath Company, Benton Harbor, Michigan
Hewlett-Packard, Colorado Springs, Colorado
Radio Corporation of America, Harrison, New Jersey
Texas Instruments, Dallas, Texas
Zenith Radio Corp., Chicago, Illinois

Robert L. Goodman

Pineville, La.

Contents

CHAPTER 1

Why Use a Triggered Scope?

In this day and age of increasing complex electronic devices you need the most advanced test instruments available for fast, efficient diagnosis (plus a big portion of extra-sensory perception!). Certainly ranking high on any such list is a good wideband service scope and an electronic switch or a dual-trace scope. I have used the flip-flop type switch many times for testing procedures. The only problem that may occur with a scope/switch combination (as opposed to the dual-trace scope) is some instability of the dual trace and some interaction of the alternating traces. However, there are some instances when a dual-trace scope can't be beat; for example, when it comes to finding a slight degree of distortion in a stereo amplifier or other minute defect in TV receiver circuits. Consequently, the accuracy provided by a triggered scope can reduce your service time considerably.

One of the reasons for writing this book (it's hoped) is to stimulate and develop interest in the use of this advanced type test instrument. Contrary to prevailing opinion in some quarters, used professional triggered scopes can be purchased at a reasonable cost. Since they are generally built to military specifications, or you might say "built like a battleship," most are in good working condition. And a considerable amount of oscilloscope circuit knowledge can be gained by overhauling one of these instruments, as has been my own experience. In many cases about all you need do is re-tube them and clean the switches and controls.

The Advantages of a Triggered Scope

First off, a triggered scope has an excellent voltage-regulated power supply, as shown in Fig. 1-1. This makes for a very stable wavetrace, which eliminates, right off the bat,

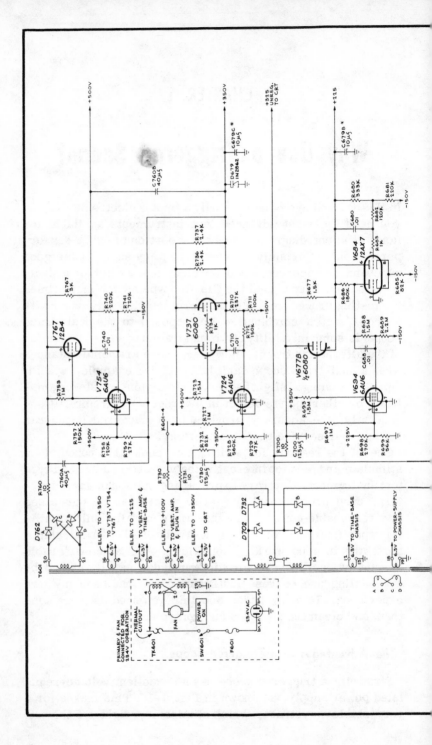

8

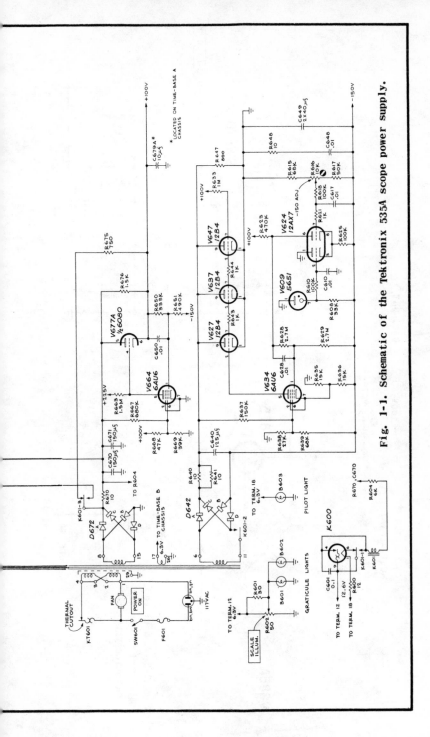

Fig. 1-1. Schematic of the Tektronix 535A scope power supply.

9

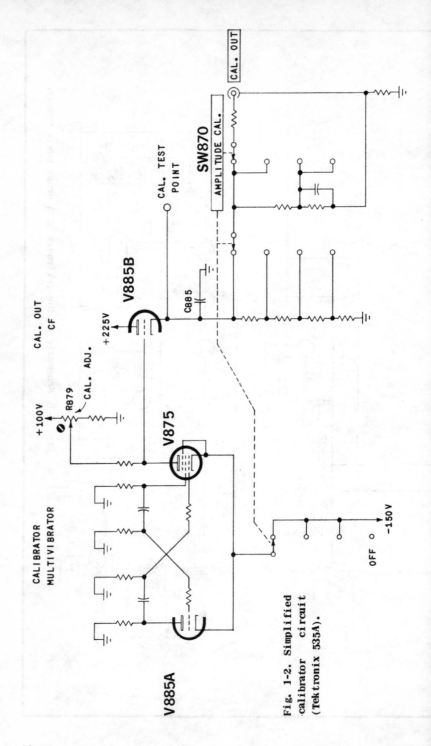

Fig. 1-2. Simplified calibrator circuit (Tektronix 535A).

a complaint registered by many technicians when asked why they don't use a scope in everyday electronic troubleshooting. Many times I've heard technicians complain that the wave-trace on most service-type scopes jumps all over the CRT. I have used all types of scopes from the top to the bottom of the barrel, and most technicians cannot be blamed for not using them.

Another thing: A professional or lab-type scope has built-in p-p voltage and sweep-calibration features, which means the vertical and horizontal amplifiers may be calibrated in volts per cm (centimeters) or time per division (time/div., in seconds, milliseconds, or microseconds). Thus, pulse duration and pulse rise time can be measured. The p-p calibrator is a square-wave generator whose approximately 1-kHz output is available at a front-panel connector labeled "cal. out." It consists of a multivibrator connected as a cathode follower to switch between two operating states—cutoff and conduction. During the negative portion of the waveform the tube is driven well below cutoff with the cathode resting at ground potential. For the positive portion of the waveform the plate rests at about + 100 volts. This plate voltage—at tube cutoff—is determined by the setting of the "cal. adj." control found on the front panel, which is part of a divider connected between regulated + 100 volts and ground. See Fig. 1-2 for a simplified calibrator circuit. The square-wave output voltage is also used to adjust the scope test probe capacitor for optimum high-frequency response compensation.

The Triggered Sweep

As suggested by the name, the waveshape or pulse you are checking actually triggers the horizontal sweep sawtooth oscillator (time-base generator) into action. And this really makes for a rock-steady wavetrace display. Some scopes have a delay line in the vertical amplifier so the pulse that triggers the sweep may be viewed on the CRT also. Actually, the time-base generator is a non-repetitive (non-free-running) multivibrator, or a "single-shot" triggered generator. The regular time-base sawtooth deflection signal is generated only when a sync signal (trigger pulse signal) is applied. When there is no trigger pulse, the scope screen is blank.

The horizontal sweep can be triggered either by a pulse

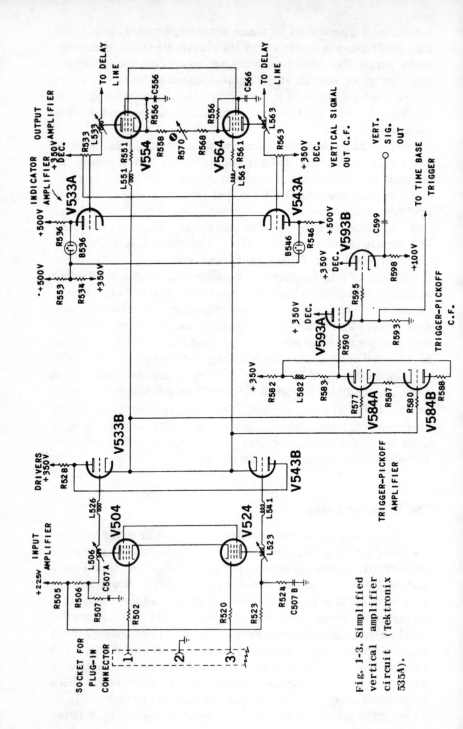

Fig. 1-3. Simplified vertical amplifier circuit (Tektronix 535A).

taken from the vertical amplifier (internal) or by an external pulse fed into the scope to trigger the time-base generator (the desired function is selected by a front-panel control). When internal triggering of the time-base generator is desired, a "sample" of the vertical signal is used to develop the triggering pulse. This "sample" is obtained from the trigger pickoff circuit consisting of the trigger pick-off amplifier and trigger pick-off cathode follower. Fig. 1-3 is a simplified ver-

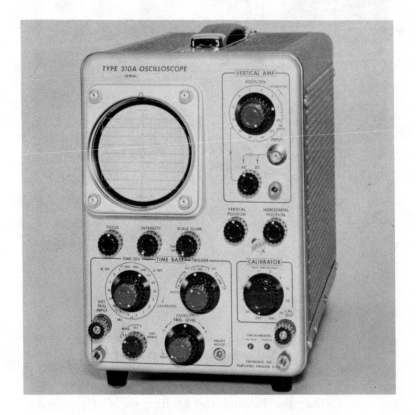

Fig. 1-4. Tektronix Type 310A portable oscilloscope.

sion of the vertical amplifier circuit used in Tektronix's Type 535A scope. A "sample" of the vertical signal is also AC-coupled to a front-panel jack, labeled "vert. sig. out," and is then fed to the time-base or horizontal sawtooth sweep generator to start the sweep across the face of the CRT. In other words, the horizontal sweep is triggered into action by the application of a pulse-type voltage, either internal or ex-

Fig. 1-5. Hickok Model 770A oscilloscope.

ternal. Of course, the time-base generator may be set for "free running" just the same as with a typical service scope. On a free-running sweep the rise and fall time of a square wave cannot be measured because the edges would be compressed. Also, the leading and trailing edge of the square wave cannot be expanded. The horizontal deflection system input can be set to any value with no overlapping of the signal display. Plus, a small portion of a waveform can be easily expanded. For example, a color burst signal can be more easily observed with a triggered-sweep scope. To view a TV horizontal waveshape display you may trigger the scope with the pulse from the flyback transformer if you wish. Other rapid pulse forms, whether they appear at regular or irregular intervals, can be observed on this type of scope. A triggered sweep can be started at any point along the signal input time base so the leading edge, lagging edge, or any portion of the signal segment may be viewed. As stated before, the scope display will be rock-steady, with no sync control to play with. You also can observe vertical integration and horizontal differentiation circuit operation very well with the triggered scope.

A Look at Some Triggered Scopes

A small portable Tektronix Type 310A scope is shown in Fig. 1-4. This precision three-inch number is lightweight and very small. Thanks to its moderate power requirements you can operate the instrument in locations that you may have considered impractical for a scope. The regulated DC power supply maintains the scope's accuracy under even very poor line-voltage regulation. The wide range of sweep speed, good sensitivity, moderate passband and ease of maintenance all combine to make the 310A a very versatile general-purpose test instrument.

The vertical amplifier deflection sensitivity is .1 volt/div., DC-coupled, with a rise time of .09 microsecond. The horizontal deflection system has 18 calibrated sweep rates and a 5x trace magnifier. Internal triggering signal requirements call for one-half division of deflection, and external triggering may be achieved with a signal varying from .2 volt to 20 volts. A voltage calibrator is provided at the front jack with 11 fixed voltages from .05 volts to 100 volts peak-to-peak. The triggered sweep and vertical amplifier response is flat from DC up to 4 MHz. This is indeed a little jewel and nice to have around the service shop!

The Hickok Model 770A (shown in Fig. 1-5) oscilloscope is a rugged, accurate instrument especially designed for the professional technician. Some of the Model 770A's design features are: 5-inch flat-fact CRT; 18 calibrated sweep rates, accurate to within 3%, from 0.5 sec/cm to 1 microsecond/cm (with 5x expansion to 0.2 microsecond/cm; a calibrated vertical amplifier with a sensitivity of .01 volts/cm to 50 volts/cm; trigger controlled sweeps; and a 4-MHz response to provide time-pulse reproduction. The internal trigger uses a one-half cm vertical signal, while the external trigger needs 0.2 volts p-p. A square-wave p-p voltage calibrator is also

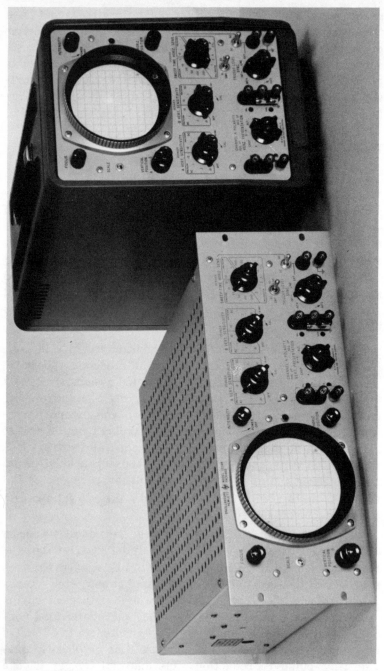

Fig. 1-6. Hewlett Packard Model 122A in self-contained cabinet (r) and rack-mounted version Model 122AR.

Fig. 1-7. Model 150A Hewlett Packard oscilloscope with dual-trace amplifier plug-in unit pulled out for inspection.

standard equipment. Shown in Fig. 1-6 is a Hewlett Packard Model 122A scope in a separate cabinet and at the left a Model 122AR rack-mounted scope.

Scopes Using Plug-In Amplifiers

Illustrated in Fig. 1-7 is a Model 150A Hewlett Packard DC-to-10-MHz general purpose oscilloscope employing a

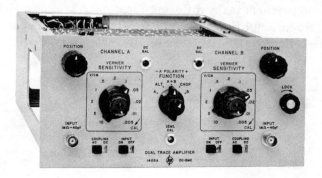

Fig. 1-8. Hewlett Packard Model 1405A dual-trace amplifier.

Fig. 1-9. Hewlett Packard time-base generators. Model 1420A (1, top) 10-MHz triggering, sweeps to 50 ns/cm, automatic triggering; Model 1422A (2) — 500-kHz triggering, sweeps to 200 ns/cm, automatic triggering; Model 1423A — 20-MHz triggering, sweeps to 20 ns/cm, trigger hold-off.

mono-accelerator type CRT and plug-in amplifier construction. Fig. 1-7 shows the dual-trace amplifier plug-in unit pulled out for inspection. This scope can be used with either internal or external sweeps which can be synchronized either internally or externally. The horizontal amplifier has a magnification circuit capable of expanding basic internal sweeps up to 100 times. The internal sweep range extends from .02 microsecond/cm to 15 second/cm.

The Model 150A uses a variety of vertical amplifier plug-in units to perform many different functions. A wideband 1405A dual-trace amplifier is shown in Fig. 1-8. The dual-trace presentation can be displayed on alternate sweeps or by chop-

Fig. 1-10. Hewlett Packard high-sensitivity deflection amplifiers; Model 1400A (1) and Model 1401A.

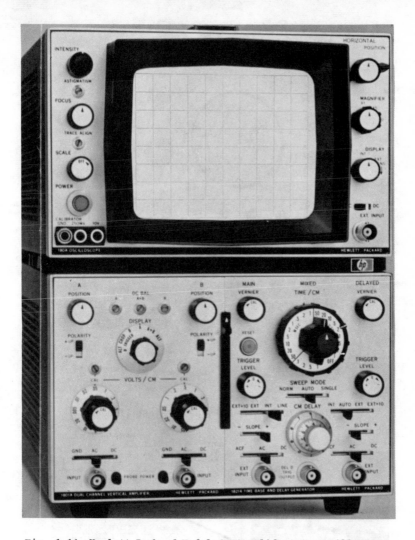

Fig. 1-11. Hewlett Packard Model 180A solid-state oscilloscope.

ping between the two input signals on the same sweep at a 100-kHz rate. In addition to single-trace presentations of channel A or B, the two channels may be algebraically added or, by a reversal of the channel A polarity switch, the differential signal may be viewed. Fig. 1-9 shows three different types of time-base plug-in units. These are used for time-interval displays.

Illustrated in Fig. 1-10 are two high-sensitivity amplifiers, Types 1400A and 1401A; both also are dual-trace triggering

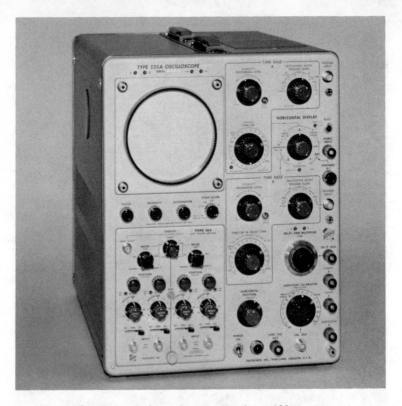

Fig. 1-12. Tektronix Type 535A oscilloscope.

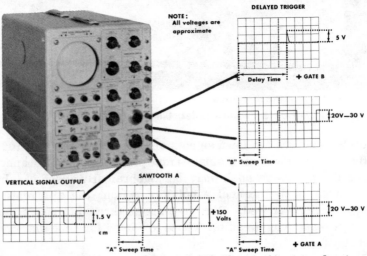

Fig. 1-13. Output waveforms available at the scope front panel (Tektronix 535A).

amplifiers. These units have a narrow bandwidth but the deflection sensitivity is 100 microvolt/cm to 20 volt/cm in 17 ranges and they each have a built-in internal calibrator.

Now should you want to go first class, look at Hewlett Packard's all solid-state scope with a vertical amplifier sensitivity of DC to 50 MHz. You can carry it around with you on service calls—it weighs only 30 pounds. However, it may set you back a few bills. Fig. 1-11 shows the Model 180A HP rugged lightweight instrument.

The Tektronix Type 535A oscilloscope is a wide-range, general purpose laboratory instrument providing accurate measurements in the DC-to-15-MHz range. The Type 535A shown in Fig. 1-12 can be operated with any Tektronix letter-series plug-in to satisfy the requirements for virtually any applica-

Fig. 1-14. Tektronix vertical amplifier plug-in units—
the O unit (l); the M unit (c), and the Z unit.

tion. Special circuits incorporated in the Type 535A scope permit an accurate, continuously variable delay in the presentation of the sweep from 1 microsecond to 10 seconds after receipt of a triggering impulse. This feature permits observation of a small portion of the normal sweep, accurate measurement of waveform jitter, precise time measurements, plus many other uses. The 535A has sweep rates of 1 microsecond to 5 seconds per cm in 24 accurately calibrated steps. For internal triggering a 2 millimeter signal is required, while for external triggering a signal from 0.2 volts to 10 volts is needed. A delayed sweep can be used and the magnifier provides a 5x magnification of the center 2-centimeter portion of the CRT display. An external horizontal input is provided, as well as a sawtooth voltage output jack on the front panel which can be used for coil ringing checks. Shown in Fig. 1-13 are the many output waveforms available at the scope's front panel.

Three basic plug-in units are shown in Fig. 1-14. The Q Type unit can be operated with strain gauges and other transducers. The unit provides high gain, low noise, and extremely low drift. The Type Z plug-in unit extends the accuracy of voltage measurements. It is used in three modes of operation: (1) as a conventional preamplifier, (2) as a differential input preamp, or (3) as a calibrated differential comparator. The M Type unit allows the display of from one to

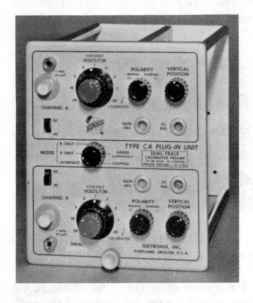

Fig. 1-15. Tektronix Type CA dual-trace DC-coupled plug-in unit.

four signals, separately or in any configuration. Both chopped and alternate electronic switching are available. Great for isolating tough intermittent circuit malfunctions! The Type CA dual-trace DC-coupled plug-in amplifier shown in Fig. 1-15 is one unit many TV service technicians can put to good use. It contains two identical input channels, either of which can be operated separately. The two channels can be electronically switched, either at a chopped rate of about 100 kHz or triggered by the scope's own sweep. In addition, both channels can be combined at the output, adding or subtracting according to the settings of the polarity switches.

22

Dual Switching Inputs

The ideal dual-input amplifier will pass either of two input signals, one at a time, to permit viewing either signal without distrubing connections. Comparison of the two signals is thereby permitted. Manual switching, available on some instruments, is the simplest method but electronic switching

Fig. 1-16. The Hewlett Packard Model 152A dual-trace amplifier shown in operation.

permits simultaneous viewing of two or more signals. Since the two signals are displayed separately, scopes with built-in electronic switches are commonly called dual-trace scopes. They should not be confused with dual-beam scopes. Dual-trace scopes offer some advantages over dual-beam scopes, and vice versa. Two simultaneous or recurrent signals of

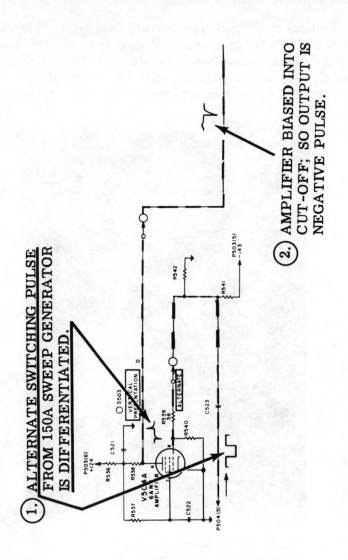

1. ALTERNATE SWITCHING PULSE FROM 150A SWEEP GENERATOR IS DIFFERENTIATED.

2. AMPLIFIER BIASED INTO CUT-OFF; SO OUTPUT IS NEGATIVE PULSE.

Fig. 1-17. Simplified schematic of Hewlett Packard's switching circuitry.

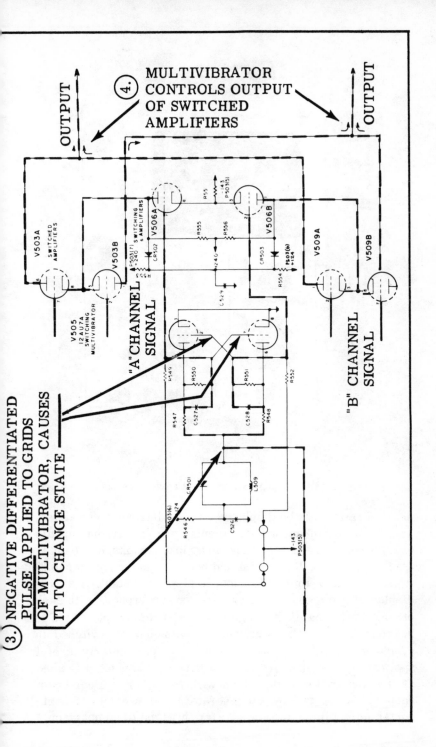

③ NEGATIVE DIFFERENTIATED PULSE APPLIED TO GRIDS OF MULTIVIBRATOR, CAUSES IT TO CHANGE STATE

④ MULTIVIBRATOR CONTROLS OUTPUT OF SWITCHED AMPLIFIERS

OUTPUT

OUTPUT

"A" CHANNEL SIGNAL

"B" CHANNEL SIGNAL

V503A
SWITCHED AMPLIFIERS

V503B

V505
12AU7A
SWITCHING
MULTIVIBRATOR

V506A

V506B

V509A

V509B

SWITCHING
6 AMPLIFIERS

25

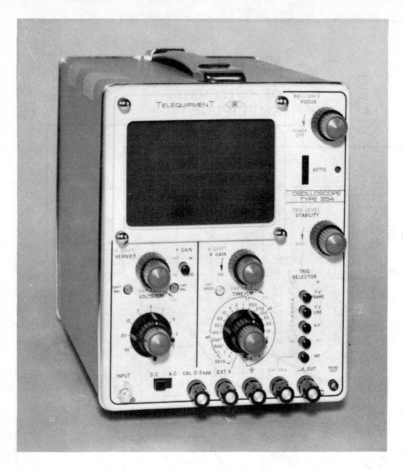

Fig. 1-18. Telequipment Model S54 oscilloscope.

short duration may be displayed on a dual-trace scope. Also, some dual-beam scopes can display non-recurrent signals on different time bases. The principal advantages of dual-trace scopes are lower cost and better comparison capabilities. A split-beam oscilloscope is also very useful. A steady display of two signals, which are not synchronous with each other, is the main advantage of a dual-trace scope. This is possible because the triggering signals may be switched in synchronism with the input signals. A particularly useful application of such a display is where one waveform is used as a standard for comparison with the other. Dual-beam scopes, having two sweep generators and two sets of horizontal deflection plates, also offer this type of comparison.

Electronic switches should be capable of two switching modes —rapidly during sweeps, or synchronously during sweep retrace intervals. The first is called "chopped," the second "alternate." The alternate mode is used more frequently and is preferred for displays employing faster sweeps. The chopped mode is used for comparing low-frequency recurrent signals or longer time durations. When displaying two very bright traces using the chopped mode, the display may show the chopping waveform transients as faint lines connecting the two traces. Some scopes blank (turn off) the CRT beam during these transition intervals to prevent them from appearing in the display. The chopping rate (frequency) should be as high as possible, as long as the resulting traces are not broadened significantly by distortion of the chopping signal. When the chopped mode is used with relatively fast non-recurrent sweeps, the traces are not continuous but are made up of separated segments; the number of segments depending on the chopping rate and sweep duration. For instance, if the chopping rate is 100 kHz and the sweep duration is 1 millisecond, there will be 100 segments in each trace. How well these separate segments depict all the detail in the two waveforms limits the usefulness of the chopped mode, compared to an alternately switched display or a dual-beam scope.

Dual-Trace Theory

Let's look at how the dual-trace amplifier operates. The Hewlett Packard Model 152A dual-trace amplifier (Fig. 1-16) contains two identical amplifiers. Each amplifier channel has an input-sensitivity range switch and a trace-positioning circuit. The signal from either channel is fed through separate push-pull cathode followers to the main vertical amplifier in the oscilloscope. Fig. 1-17 shows a simplified switching schematic. All stages are direct coupled. For AC coupling, blocking capacitors are switched in ahead of the input attenuators.

The input attenuators control the vertical sensitivity of the amplifier channels. The first stage of the dual-channel amplifier consists of a push-pull cathode follower; one side receives the input signal through the polarity switch; the input to the other side is bypassed to ground. The balance control adjusts the grid bias on one side of the phase inverter so the

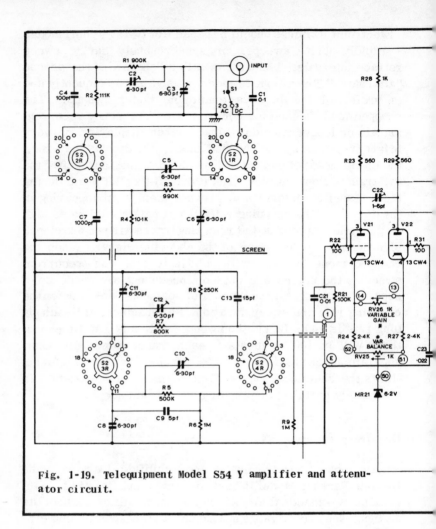

Fig. 1-19. Telequipment Model S54 Y amplifier and attenuator circuit.

trace will remain stationary when the vernier control is varied. This requires that the bias on the two tubes remains unchanged, which in turn requires that the vernier gain control be connected between points having no DC potential difference. The balance control adjusts the grid bias to one side of the phase inverter so that this condition is met. The two cathodes of the second stage are coupled through the vernier and calibrate potentiometers, which vary the cathode-to-cathode coupling, introduce cathode degeneration to vary the gain, and permit the stage to act as a phase inverter. The spot is positioned by varying the DC level equally and oppositely on the two plates

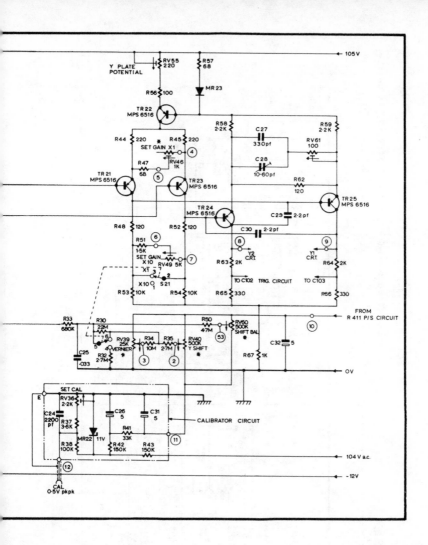

of the phase inverter. The DC levels, as well as the signals, are then direct-coupled to the following amplifiers to prevent changes in cathode currents when the position controls are varied; part of the positioning voltage is fed back to each cathode.

The third stage of the unit is a switched amplifier which can be turned on or off manually by the vertical presentation switch or rapidly during alternate or chopped operation. The plate circuits of both the A and B channels are common but do not interact because the amplifiers cannot operate simultaneously. The dual-channel amplifier also has a switching

29

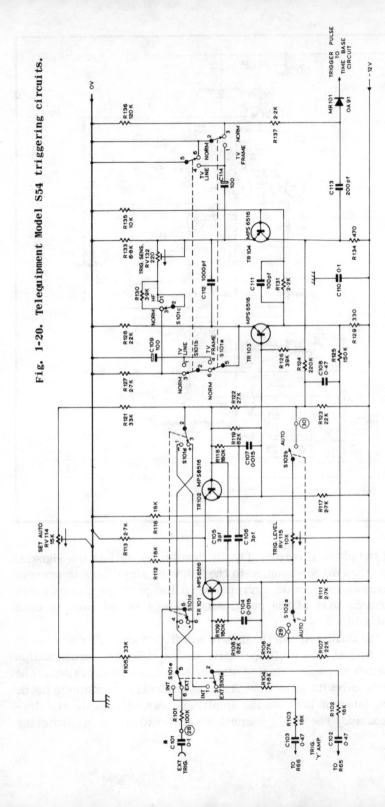

Fig. 1-20. Telequipment Model S54 triggering circuits.

multivibrator for turning each channel off and on during chopped and alternate operation. For chopped operation, the switching multivibrator free-runs at approximately 100 kHz, switching each channel off and on at this rate. During chopped operation a fast negative pulse from the switching multivibrator is amplified and inverted through V504A and V504B and applied to the CRT cathode so that the lines between the two traces are blanked out. For alternate operation, a high negative bias converts the free-running multivibrator to a bistable flip-flop. At the end of each sweep a signal from the sweep generator switches the multivibrator from one channel to the other, thus providing alternate presentation on the scope CRT.

Here's a brand new scope with big features that would look good on your bench. It's the new Telequipment S54 (shown in Fig. 1-18) oscilloscope manufactured by an English concern, acquired by Tektronix, Inc., as a lower-priced line. Some labs, service shops, or schools would like to have Tektronix scopes but find the price tag too high. With a few less features the $350 price of this little scope is just right, quite competitive with some lab scope kits.

The scope is a solid-state, triggered-sweep instrument with a 6 by 10 cm CRT. The vertical amplifier is flat from DC to 10 MHz, which covers the needs of color TV servicing. The system rise time is 35 ns, which gives good resolution for pulse circuit analysis. The calibrated deflection sensitivity is 0.1v/cm to 50v/cm ($\pm 5\%$), controlled by a convenient 1-2-5 sequence step selector. A 10x amplifier is included to increase the deflection factor to 10 mv/cm, at a reduced bandwidth (DC to 4 MHz).

The horizontal features, most significantly, include a triggered sweep, thus providing the means to select the point on the waveform where the sweep starts so that you may effectively stop the trace and make measurements with the calibrated graticule. The S54 has both automatic and stability/trigger level modes. The triggering signal is available from either the internal vertical amplifier (see the schematic in Fig. 1-19) or an external connector and, most important to the service industry, it has provision for TV frame and line triggering. The sweep rates are calibrated from 0.2 microsecond/cm to 2 second/cm ($\pm 5\%$), and to approximately 40 ns uncalibrated through the use of the X gain control, which is a variable mag-

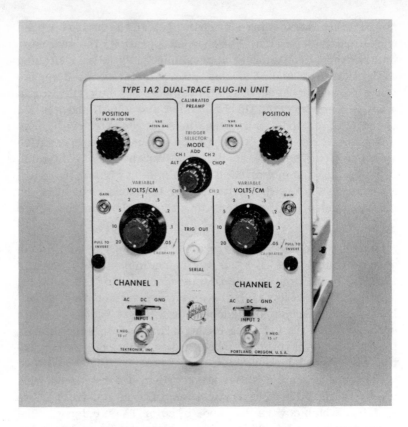

Fig. 1-21. Tektronix Model 1A2 dual-trace plug-in amplifier.

nifier. The display section employs a 5-inch rectangular CRT. To prevent trace drift with supply voltage change there is a heater stabilizer for the nuvistor input stages.

The internal trigger pickoff amplifier (see Fig. 1-20) is also balanced to reduce ripple effect on trigger operation, particularly at high frequencies. All stages use silicon transistors. Even the HV power supply (4KV) uses solid-state diodes.

The circuit was designed and laid out on one large circuit board, with all components mounted on one side to provide ease of servicing and flow soldering in production. The fiberglass board has about 800 holes punched in one operation, assembled, and then mounted in the chassis, which makes for a very rugged instrument. A cable connects all off-the-board components, such as front and rear panel controls and CRT connections. The total weight of the oscilloscope is 17 lbs; power consumption is 30 va; dimensions are 9" high x 7" wide x 16" deep. Very easy to carry around on your service calls. Shown in Fig. 1-21 is the 1A2 Tektronix dual-trace plug-in amplifier. This is the new replacement for the older CA type amplifier unit.

CHAPTER 2

AC-DC and Dual-Beam Oscilloscopes

Most modern professional oscilloscopes have DC-coupled deflection systems. This not only provides undistorted and unattenuated response to low-frequency signals but is useful when examining fast signals. For example, when checking vacuum tube circuits, you can determine to what DC levels plate or screen voltages swing when complex signals occur at these electrodes. Just for the record, a calibrated DC scope makes a very accurate VTVM for testing DC and any p-p AC voltage riding on it, all at the same time—a big $ervice time $aver.

Not too many years ago DC scopes were used only in research and laboratory work. However, new engineering design and technological advancement now makes it practical for many manufacturers and kit makers to build lower priced DC scopes. Is the DC scope actually better than the AC-only type instrument? Well, let's look and see.

What Makes the DC Scope Different

An AC scope has a blocking capacitor somewhere between the input terminal and the input element of the first-stage amplifier. This then isolates the input amplifier from any DC voltage that may be present in the circuit being tested, but permits the AC signal to pass onto the scope's vertical plates. The usual high-gain AC amplifier is then used for the vertical signal amplification.

The input blocking capacitor is eliminated in the DC scope, and the input terminal is connected directly to the input of the first amplifier stage. Both the existing DC potential and AC signal appear as vertical deflection on the oscilloscope screen. Most DC scopes have provisions for an AC input; the input circuit has a blocking capacitor and a switch that shorts it out for DC operation. When the capacitor is shorted, the DC mode is selected and both AC and DC voltages are fed to the vertical amplifier. This feature is one reason for the higher cost.

Since there are no coupling capacitors, the grid of each tube operates at a DC potential equal to that of the plate of the preceding tube, and since the plate voltage of an amplifier tube must be more positive than the grid voltage of the tube, we must generally provide the plate circuit of each succeeding tube with a positive voltage greater than the voltage provided for the preceding plate circuit. We can consider this special power supply requirement as the price we pay for the ability to amplify DC and very-low-frequency information. The DC amplifier doesn't know the difference between a power supply variation or the input voltage variation. Even the best DC scopes are more prone to drift, since the input tubes are not isolated from the power supply as in the AC-coupled scope amplifier. When a DC-coupled amplifier is not passing information, the input circuit rests at a no-signal or "quiescent" DC voltage determined by the quiescent DC voltage of the signal source. We call this no-signal voltage the DC level of the input circuit. This input DC level might be ground level (zero volts), or it may be some positive or negative DC voltage.

High-gain DC-coupled amplifiers are going to drift somewhat. After turn-on, an hour or so is sometimes required for the rate of drift to reduce to a minimum. After warmup, the maximum amount of drift to be expected is often specified in terms of millivolts (or microvolts) per hour. The amount of position change that the drift represents depends upon the deflection factor selected. For example, if the deflection factor is 1 mv/cm and the drift specification is 1 mv/hr, the drift in any one-hour period should not be greater than 1 cm. In the vast majority of cases, the drift per hour is of little significance, since scope checks generally take no more than a minute or so.

How long the balance and position controls, which interact somewhat, will operate properly without any internal adjustments is also important. Unfortunately, this is nearly impossible to predict, so again, experience is the best teacher for sound judgment; one side-by-side comparison of two types of scopes may not be adequate.

Scopes You May Want

Fig. 2-1. Knight KG-2100 DC scope.

Fig. 2-2. Tektronix Type 310 (bottom left) AC-DC triggered 3-inch oscilloscope.

Fig. 2-3. Low-cost Heathkit Model 10-10 AC-DC 3-inch scope, also available in kit or factory assembled form.

A Zero Reference Point

When using a DC scope you are always assured of an accurate zero reference point, but with an AC scope you are never quite sure. Now, if you remove all input signals to a DC scope, ground the vertical input probe, and set the trace line to the center of the screen with the vertical position control; this centerline will be your zero reference point. A trace above the center line is positive and a trace below is negative.

Now, let's assume you want to measure a sine wave which has a 30v p-p amplitude, beginning from zero and rising to 30 volts. You can measure both 30-volt values on either the AC or DC scopes; however, the AC scope cannot tell if the

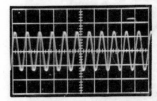

Fig. 2-4. 30v p-p sine wave measured on an AC scope. Notice that it is centered around the average waveform voltage.

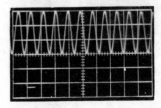

Fig. 2-5. 30v p-p sine wave measured on a DC scope. Notice the bottom peaks rest on the centerline (zero reference).

vertical rise begins at zero or at some other DC voltage level. Nor will it tell you the true p-p voltage. For example, set an AC scope for 10v deflection for each vertical division mark on the CRT. Use the center of the screen as a zero reference line. The sine wave you should see is shown in Fig. 2-4. The waveshape covers three vertical divisions to show the 30v p-p reading. But this is no indication that the trace begins at zero. Because you do not know where zero is, you may think that zero is at the center reference line of the screen. You could then assume, incorrectly, that the sine wave begins at the 15-volts position, then drops down to 15-volts negative.

With a DC scope hooked to the same circuit (all conditions the same as for the AC scope) the resultant trace is shown in

Fig. 2-5. The sine wave begins at the reference line, or zero, and rises 3 divisions, indicating a 30v p-p potential. Please remember that on the AC scope the trace will center itself around the waveform's average voltage, thus making it hard to establish the true zero point because the trace will reposition itself with changes in waveform shapes. Half the effective waveform voltage always falls above the no-signal trace, while the other half always falls below. For example, look at a 50-volt p-p TV horizontal drive pulse at the grid of the horizontal output tube. On an AC scope (set for 20v deflection per division) a waveshape similar to Fig. 2-6 will appear. With all conditions the same, but using a DC scope, you can see in Fig. 2-7 that a negative 60 volts DC is also

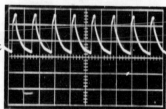

Fig. 2-6. Horizontal drive pulse waveform as it appears on an AC scope. At 20 volts per division, the p-p voltage is 50v.

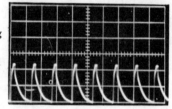

Fig. 2-7. Same drive pulse appearing in Fig. 2-6, measured on a DC scope. Notice the 60-volt negative DC level (20v per division).

present at the grid of the horizontal output tube. Knowing that, you won't have to reach for the VTVM to measure this DC voltage.

Faster Measurements

With the DC scope both the DC level and AC signal voltage in the circuit can be measured simultaneously. Let's suppose you want to measure the signal at the base of a transistor amplifier stage, and at the same time check the DC level at this same point. If you have only an AC scope you must use a VTVM for the DC level, and then use the scope for a check of the signal wavetrace. If you had a DC scope, both checks can be made simultaneously. For a practical application of this example, let's look at the transistor video amplifier stage of a Zenith 20YIC48 color chassis. (See Fig. 2-8 for a partial schematic of the video amplifier stages.) To see how this method works, notice in Fig. 2-9 the double exposure of wave-shapes at the base and emitter of transistor TR1. With the oscilloscope set for DC, and using the bottom line of the graticule for zero-volts reference, the bottom wavetrace appeared at the base of TR1. Notice this reads about 2 volts DC with a 2.5-volt AC p-p video signal. (The vertical amplifier sensitivity was set for 2 volts per cm/division.) The top video waveshape is 10 volts DC and the video signal is approximately 6 volts p-p. Notice the signal phase inversion.

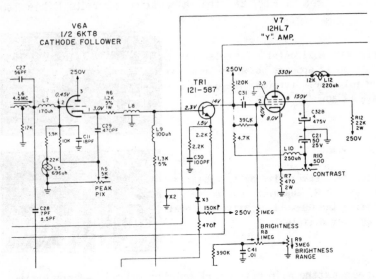

Fig. 2-8. Video amplifier circuit in Zenith's 20YIC48 chassis.

If these same signals had been observed with an AC scope, the traces would be in the same position on the screen and only the video signal amplitude would have changed. You could not tell what the DC voltage was without meter measurements. However, the capability of measuring AC and DC simultaneously on a DC scope is not always an advantage. This will become apparent should the average DC voltage level not be within the same range as the AC. If the voltages are not, you may not be able to see them both (or measure them accurately) without switching vertical gain or repositioning the scope trace. For instance, assume you want to measure a 25-volt p-p AC signal on the plate element of a vacuum tube with a 250-volt DC potential; if you set the vertical gain to 30-volt p-p full scale for the AC waveform, you would have to reposition the trace vertically in order to bring it down into view. Thus, the advantage of simultaneous measurement is somewhat limited.

Low-Frequency Cutoff Point

Any AC scope must have a low-frequency cutoff point, perhaps as low as 3 or 4 Hz. Still, it represents a fixed limit. As this point is approached, the input signal amplitude will be reduced. If the low limit is 4 Hz, for example, you might notice some amplitude drop at 15 Hz. Some scope manufacturers offset this by specifying the low-frequency limit in their AC scopes well above the actual cutoff point. This may be a good practice but it's possible the technician will not know

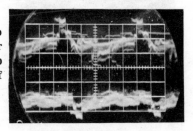

Fig. 2-9. The top trace is a 10v p-p video signal measured at the emitter of TR1. Bottom trace is a 2.5v p-p video signal appearing at the base of TR1. (Vertical amplifier, 2v/cm, positive up).

the exact frequency of the signal he is measuring or will not remember the scope's lower limitation. Either way, you could have an error without knowing it.

Wavetrace Distortion

A DC scope is not as apt to produce distortion, particularly at low frequencies. Whenever a waveshape of long duration (low frequency) is displayed on an AC scope, some distortion occurs. It is caused by the nonlinear charge and discharge rates of the coupling capacitors in the vertical amplifier stage. Sharp rise step voltages can be a problem here. Amplifiers that are AC coupled do not respond correctly to step voltages of long duration because these waveforms are differentiated (like rectangular pulses, square waves, and staircase waveforms, for an example). After each initial vertical deflection the waveshape starts to slope (see Fig. 2-10) exponentially toward the zero position, depending on the charge of the RC coupling networks. In an amplifier, the coupling capacitors must be charged and discharged to pass each square-wave pulse (or any pulse with a sharp vertical rise or fall). If the waveshapes are short in duration (a few microseconds), as with high-frequency signals, they would use only a short portion of the capacitor charge-discharge curve and therefore would appear without any distortion. As the signal pulse time lengthens, however, the natural curve becomes more noticeable, affecting the waveform more appreciably.

Because no coupling capacitors are used in the vertical de-

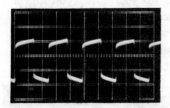

Fig. 2-10. Square wave showing low-frequency distortion, caused by defective coupling capacitors (observed on an AC scope).

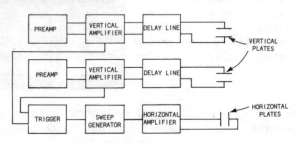

Fig. 2-11. Block diagram of a dual-trace single horizontal sweep scope.

flection amplifier of a DC scope, this type of distortion does not happen with either long or short pulses. Some AC scope manufacturers try to compensate for this type of distortion by using a low-frequency boost network in the vertical amplifier stage. This causes the waveform to slope away from zero for an interval following each step and finally levels off and slopes back toward zero. Although this is helpful, some distortion still exists. But don't let this limitation cause you to throw away your AC-only scope! They are good scopes and we have used them a good many years. But in considering a new scope, do look at the AC-DC professional triggered oscilloscope before you buy.

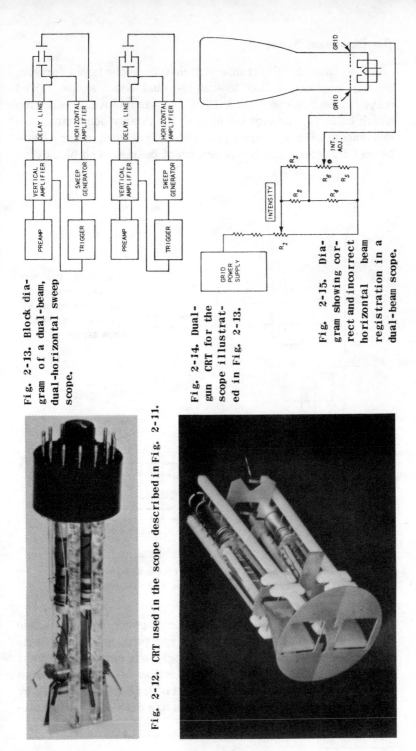

Fig. 2-13. Block diagram of a dual-beam, dual-horizontal sweep scope.

Fig. 2-14. Dual-gun CRT for the scope illustrated in Fig. 2-13.

Fig. 2-15. Diagram showing correct and incorrect horizontal beam registration in a dual-beam scope.

Fig. 2-12. CRT used in the scope described in Fig. 2-11.

43

The Dual-Beam Scope

Just in case the electronic switch-type scope is not for you, we will now take a fast look at the dual-beam scope. (And maybe dream along just a little bit, too!) An application which calls for the viewing of two, singularly occurring, simultaneous events, requires a dual-beam scope, using a dual-beam CRT which has two independent beams. The block dia-

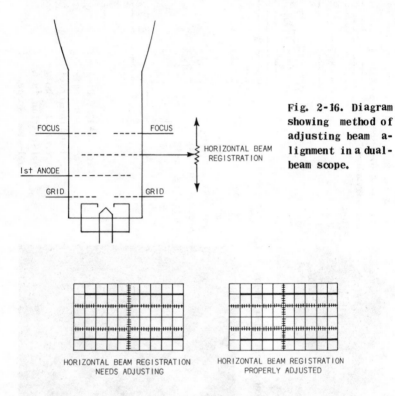

Fig. 2-16. Diagram showing method of adjusting beam alignment in a dual-beam scope.

Fig. 2-17. Diagrams showing correct and incorrect horizontal beam registration in a dual-beam scope.

gram of a dual-beam, single horizontal sweep scope is shown in Fig. 2-11. The dual-beam CRT has two guns and two sets of vertical deflection plates, but only one set of horizontal deflection plates. The gun and deflection system is shown in Fig. 2-12. These two beams may be deflected vertically by two different signals but both beams are deflected horizontally by one horizontal sweep signal.

The Dual Gun

A block diagram of a dual-beam, dual horizontal sweep os-cilloscope is shown in Fig. 2-13. Notice that each beam has independent vertical and horizontal sweep systems, and each (see Fig. 2-14 for the gun assembly) can be deflected hori-zontally at an independent sweep speed and vertically by an independent vertical signal. It is called a dual-gun CRT, since each gun is complete by itself.

In a dual-beam, single horizontal sweep oscilloscope there is usually only one front panel intensity control which sets the voltage on both CRT grids. Because of slight differences in the two gun structures some means of balancing the inten-sity of the two beams is needed. The intensity balance control

Fig. 2-18. Hewlett Packard Model 132A dual-beam scope.

or the "intensity adjust" performs this function (see Fig. 2-15). Intensity control R1 sets the voltage at the top of R2 and R3. Resistors R2 and R4 form a fixed divider that sets the voltage on the grid of the bottom gun. R3, R5, and R6 form a similar adjustable divider for the grid of the top gun. By adjusting R6 the intensity of the two beams can then be balanced. Once they are balanced the front panel control will set the intensity of both electron beams.

Horizontal Beam Registration

A dual-beam, dual horizontal sweep oscilloscope has an

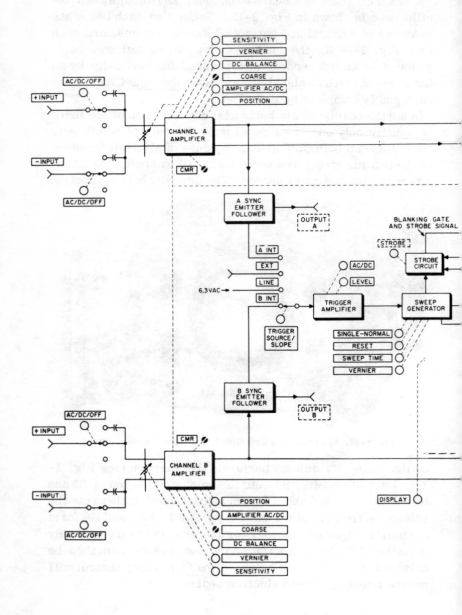

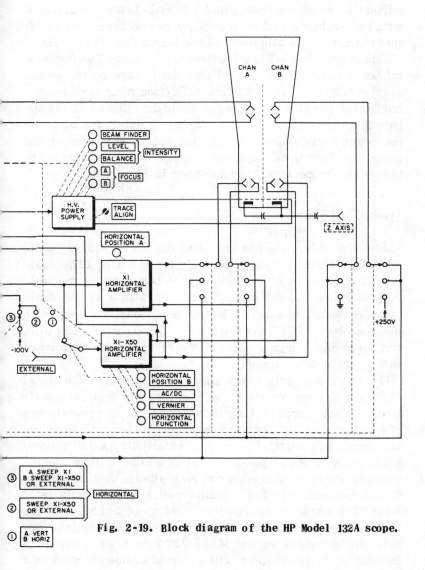

Fig. 2-19. Block diagram of the HP Model 132A scope.

intensity and focus control for each beam on the front panel, and each beam can be positioned horizontally by a positioning control. Dual-gun oscilloscopes have independent horizontal sweeps; therefore, the horizontal position of each beam is adjustable from the front panel. A dual-beam oscilloscope with but one horizontal system requires another means to adjust the horizontal alignment of the beams (see Fig. 2-16).

This is done by splitting the first anode input. The horizontal beam registration control sets the voltage on the second section of this anode. Without deflection plate blanking the horizontal position of the beam would be affected if the apparent source of the electrons were off axis. By adjusting the beam registration control, the apparent source of the beam electrons is adjusted until the horizontal position of the beams are properly aligned as shown in Fig. 2-17.

Typical Dual-Beam Scopes

Most dual-beam scopes are used for low-frequency audio or stereo checks. The Hewlett Packard Model 132A dual-beam oscilloscope (see Fig. 2-18) is basically two general-purpose, low-frequency oscilloscopes with a single dual-beam cathode-ray tube. The combined oscilloscope, with the dual-beam CRT, permits many electronic, scientific, and mechanical measurements which cannot be performed with a single-beam scope.

The two completely independent CRT beams in the Model 132A are driven vertically by two separate vertical amplifiers. Each vertical amplifier bandwidth is greater than 500-kHz at sensitivities between 1 millivolt/cm and 20 volts/cm; maximum vertical amplifier sensitivity is 100 microvolts/cm at a lower bandwidth of 200 kHz. Either single-ended or differential signals can be applied to each amplifier. Common-mode rejection of differential input signals is at least 92 db on the most sensitive input range and 30 db on the least sensitive range (20 volts/cm). Rear panel vertical outputs are provided on the Model 132A to allow convenient monitoring of the display with external equipment such as a recorder on an RMS voltmeter.

Two separate horizontal amplifiers, one for each beam, allows operation at two different sweep rates simultaneously. One of the horizontal amplifiers permits magnifying both beams concurrently, or one beam only while the other beam remains unmagnified. Magnification allows detail examination of a particular section of a waveform, and in this scope magnification is continuously adjustable up to a maximum of 50x. A 50x magnified display is equivalent to a 500-centimeter trace length. The complete overall block diagram for the Model 132A dual-beam scope is shown in Fig. 2-19. With its independent CRT beams it offers many display capabili-ties.

CHAPTER 3

Oscilloscope Control Adjustments

At one time the oscilloscope was classified as a laboratory instrument. Its relation to the troubleshooting of electronic equipment was indeed minimal. However, within recent years the advancement of electronic technology has placed a multitude of very sophisticated devices in the hands of a huge consumer's market, equipment that can no longer be serviced with yester-year techniques. This advancement has most assuredly touched the TV/electronic service field. Consequently, today's TV technicians, through necessity, are encouraged to use the oscilloscope for even routine service problems and adjustments. It provides us with a means of actually looking at voltage waveforms and how the waveform changes with time.

A Typical Triggered Scope

In order to acquaint you with the use of a professional oscilloscope, this Chapter outlines some of the more frequently encountered oscilloscope operations and control adjustments. Illustrated in Fig. 3-1 is a Hewlett Packard scope with a Model 152A dual-trace plug-in amplifier. This dual-trace oscilloscope will permit simultaneous observation of two phenomena. The scope has two identical input channels, each with a frequency response down only 3 db from DC to 10 MHz. These two channels, identified as A and B inputs, can be operated individually or simultaneously. In the simultaneous mode this scope provides a choice of electronic switching at a 100-kHz rate, or electronic switching on alternate sweeps. ("Sweep" refers to the horizontal deflection of the wavetrace.) Many other preamplifier types may be plugged into this scope. You can choose a high-gain, single-trace, a fast rise time, or a differential input plug-in unit. The differential unit provides the difference between two vertical-input signals, rejecting the common-mode signal.

Let's look at the controls and functions of the Hewlett Packard Model 150A scope with the 152A plug-in dual-trace amplifier. It may look complicated, but it's not, and it's just as easy—or more so—to set up and adjust as the common service scope. Please refer to the correlating control knobs and functions under study. (The control numbers refer to the balloon numbers in the appropriate illustration.)

Numbers 1 & 2—Sweep time/cm switch and sweep vernier. See Fig. 3-4. Select the proper horizontal sweep speed with the sweep time/cm control, and set the vernier in the "cal" position when direct reading of sweep time/cm is desired. For TV horizontal waveshape measurements set the control

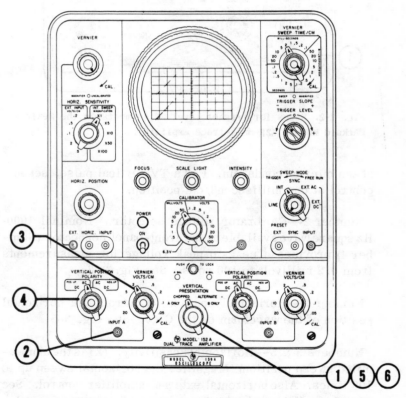

Fig. 3-1. Hewlett Packard Model 152A dual-trace plug-in amplifier operation.

95473   51

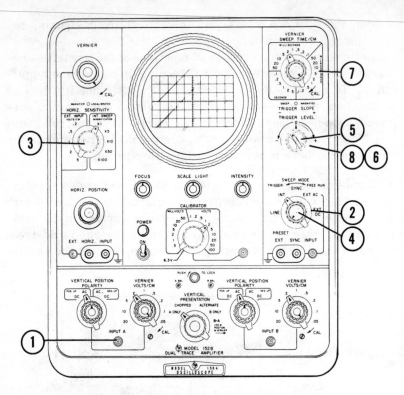

Fig. 3-2. Steps for trigger level adjustments on the Hewlett Packard Model 152B dual-trace amplifier.

at ten microseconds/cm. For a TV vertical pulse, set this control at one millisecond/cm position.

Number 2—Calibrator voltage selector. Nominal 1000-Hz square wave available at the front-panel connector (Number 4) provides a peak-to-peak voltage for measurements from 0.2 millivolt to 100 volts. See Fig. 3-6.

Number 3—Horizontal position. Controls the horizontal position of the waveform on the CRT. See Fig. 3-5.

Numbers 3 & 5—Horizontal sensitivity. (X1 is the unmagnified sweep position) Magnifies the horizontal sweep up to 100 times. Also horizontal external amplifier control. See Fig. 3-4. Notice the horizontal amplifier vernier gain located above the horizontal sensitivity control.

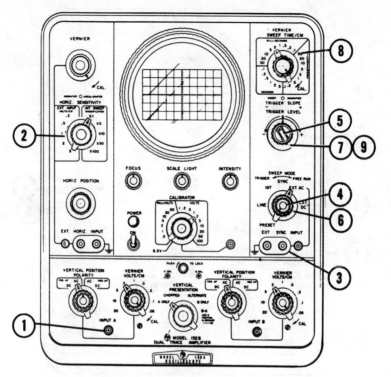

Fig. 3-3. Steps for sweep mode selection.
(Courtesy: Hewlett Packard)

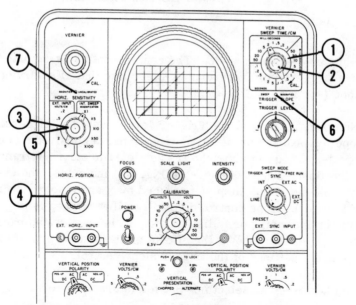

Fig. 3-4. Steps for horizontal sensitivity adjustment.
(Courtesy: Hewlett Packard)

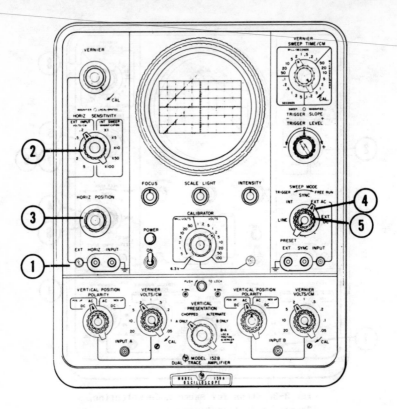

Fig. 3-5. Horizontal position adjustment.
(Courtesy: Hewlett Packard)

Number 4—Sweep mode. The center control is adjusted for a triggered or free-running sweep like that of a service scope (see Fig. 3-3).

Numbers 5, 6, and 8—Trigger level. Set the triggered slope for positive or negative triggering, as desired. See Fig. 3-2. You can adjust the trigger level to start the trace at the desired pulse level. As Fig. 3-7 indicates, the effects on the scope display produced by + and - settings of the triggering slope control determines if the sweep is triggered on the rising or falling portion of the input waveform. Fig. 3-8 further shows the effects on the display produced by + and - settings of the trigger slope control.

Number 6—Sync selector. Set for internal, external, or

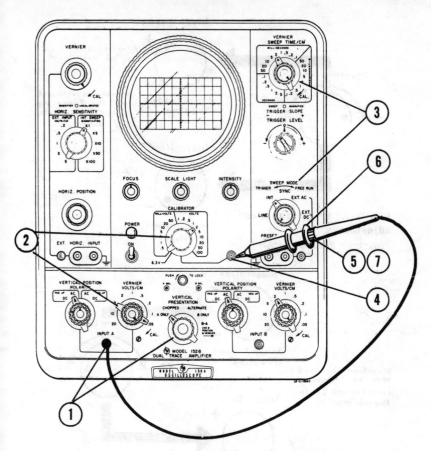

Fig. 3-6. Steps for vertical amplifier calibration.
(Courtesy: Hewlett Packard)

line sync as desired (see Fig. 3-3). In Fig. 3-9 the triggering signal may be selected from three possible sources.

Also notice the following controls in Fig. 3-1:

- Focus—Adjusts beam focus for a sharp trace.
- Scale light—Controls graticule light.
- Intensity—Controls the brightness of the electron beams.

Dual-Trace Amplifier Plug-In Unit

Numbers 1, 5, and 6—Vertical presentation. Selects

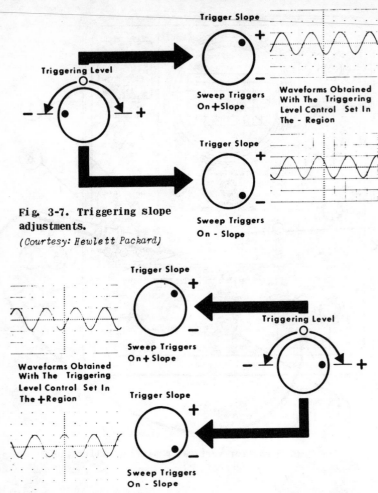

Fig. 3-7. Triggering slope
adjustments.
(Courtesy: Hewlett Packard)

either A input or B input only, or can be switched to the alternate or chopped mode for a dual-trace presentation. For the B input the controls are the same as for the A channel adjustments (Fig. 3-1).

Number 3—Volts/cm. Calibrated input ranges for the vertical amplifier gain adjustment. The vernier (small center) control permits continuous adjustment of the vertical gain.

Number 4—Polarity-input channel A, AC-DC, positive or negative pulse up. The vertical position (small center) control moves the beam trace up or down on the CRT.

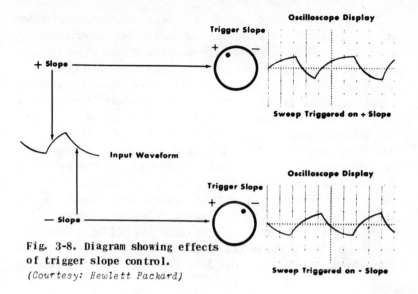

Fig. 3-8. Diagram showing effects of trigger slope control. *(Courtesy: Hewlett Packard)*

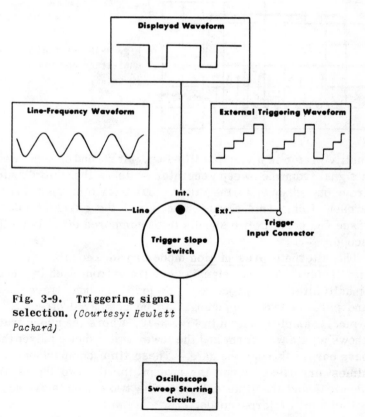

Fig. 3-9. Triggering signal selection. *(Courtesy: Hewlett Packard)*

57

The dual-trace amplifier permits simultaneous observation of two signals, which can be presented alternately or chopped, depending on the frequencies of the input signals. Chopped presentation is useful for comparing two inputs that require a slow sweep speed. In this presentation the vertical input is alternately switched between channels at a 100-kHz rate. When using either chopped or alternate sweeps for viewing related signals, the scope should be set for "ext sync" and either the A or B channel signal waveform connected to the "ext sync input" terminals. However, if the two input signals are not related in frequency, the oscilloscope may be set for "int sync." For best results with internal sync, the two traces should be as close together as possible.

The dual-channel amplifier contains a switching multivibrator for switching the two channels off and on during alternate operation. A high negative bias converts the free-running

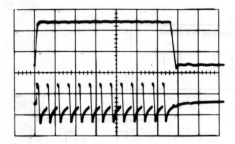

Fig. 3-10. Typical use of dual-trace operation.
(Courtesy: Hewlett Packard)

multivibrator to a bistable flip-flop. At the end of each sweep a signal from the sweep generator switches the multivibrator from one channel to the other, thus providing an alternate presentation. This arrangement gives the effect of a dual-trace and permits two signals to be compared directly on the scope.

The alternate-presentation mode provides for the alternating display of two input signals; one trace from each in a continually alternating process. This gives the dual-trace effect and permits two "happenings" to be compared directly. A typical example is shown in Fig. 3-10, where the upper trace shows a gate waveform and the lower trace shows pulses that have passed through the gate. These time comparisons are almost errorless, since the sweeps for the two inputs are identical and the time delays in the two channels are equal within 2 millimicroseconds.

The <u>chopped-presentation</u> mode is useful for comparing two inputs that require a relatively slow sweep speed. In this presentation the vertical input is alternately switched between channels at a 100-kHz rate. When the sweep repetition rate is slow, compared with the 100-kHz switching rate, the net effect is the same as with alternate presentation, except that flicker is noticeably reduced. Fig. 3-11 shows chopped operation. The chopped presentation is also useful when comparing two non-repetitive voltages. Fig. 3-12 illustrates the operation and control functions of the Tektronix type oscilloscope.

Heath-Kit Scope

Heath makes a Model IO-14 professional scope in kit form that you may wish to build, or you can buy one already built

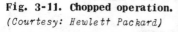
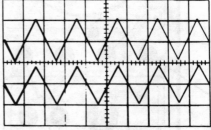

Fig. 3-11. Chopped operation.
(Courtesy: Hewlett Packard)

and calibrated. Let's take a look at this Heath lab-type triggered scope. The switches and controls on the front panel of the Model IO-14 oscilloscope are grouped and color coded for ease of operation. The paragraph numbers in this section refer to the circled numbers in Fig. 3-13.

BEAM AND SCALE CONTROLS:

1. SCALE ILLUM. When fully counterclockwise the switch on this control is in the AC power off position. As the control is rotated clockwise, the AC power is switched on, and the brightness of the edge-lighted graticule can be adjusted to the desired brillance.

2. ASTIG. This control adjusts the shape of the spot on the face of the CRT. It is used in conjunction with the focus control to obtain the sharpest, clearest display on the CRT.

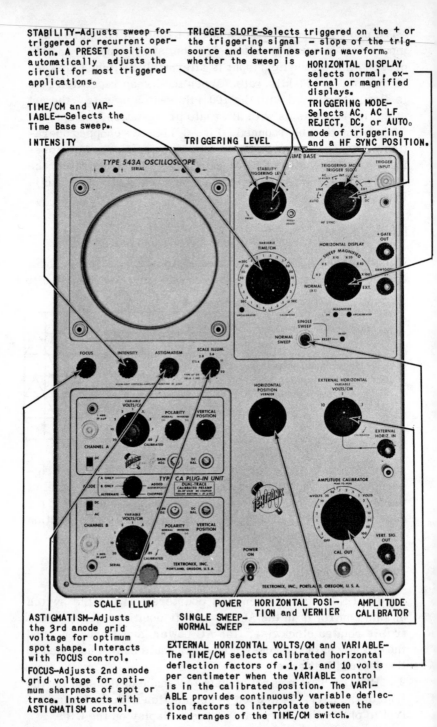

STABILITY—Adjusts sweep for triggered or recurrent operation. A PRESET position automatically adjusts the circuit for most triggered applications.

TRIGGER SLOPE—Selects triggered on the + or − slope of the triggering waveform.
the triggering signal source and determines whether the sweep is

HORIZONTAL DISPLAY selects normal, external or magnified displays.

TRIGGERING MODE—Selects AC, AC LF REJECT, DC, or AUTO. mode of triggering and a HF SYNC POSITION.

TIME/CM and VARIABLE—Selects the Time Base sweep.

INTENSITY

TRIGGERING LEVEL

ASTIGMATISM—Adjusts the 3rd anode grid voltage for optimum spot shape. Interacts with FOCUS control.

FOCUS—Adjusts 2nd anode grid voltage for optimum sharpness of spot or trace. Interacts with ASTIGMATISM control.

SCALE ILLUM

POWER

SINGLE SWEEP—
NORMAL SWEEP

HORIZONTAL POSITION and VERNIER

AMPLITUDE CALIBRATOR

EXTERNAL HORIZONTAL VOLTS/CM and VARIABLE—The TIME/CM selects calibrated horizontal deflection factors of .1, 1, and 10 volts per centimeter when the VARIABLE control is in the calibrated position. The VARIABLE provides continuously variable deflection factors to interpolate between the fixed ranges of the TIME/CM switch.

Fig. 3-12. Functions of the Tektronix Type 543 oscilloscope.

3. FOCUS. This control varies the size of the spot on the face of the CRT. The focus control is adjusted with the astig control for the sharpest display.

4. INTENSITY. The brightness of the trace is increased with clockwise rotation of the intensity control. A slight readjustment of the astig and focus controls is sometimes required after adjusting the intensity.

5. Power on indicator. Since this lamp operates from a B+ voltage, it may not go out immediately when the power is turned off.

VERTICAL AMP SECTION:

6. INPUT terminals. The coaxial socket will accept a standard coaxial connector, or a banana plug may be inserted in the center contact and a separate ground lead connected to the black binding post.

7. GAIN. This control is normally operated in its fully clockwise (cal) position. Here, the display on the CRT may be measured in terms of p-p volts by using the graticule markings and the values set by the volts/cm switch (11). It is sometimes desirable to adjust the trace to the full height of the graticule. In these instances, the gain control can be adjusted as desired; however, the display will be uncalibrated.

8. UNCAL indicator. This indicator lamp reminds the user that the vertical amplifier is uncalibrated when the gain control is not fully clockwise.

9. AC-DC coupling switch. In the AC position any DC component of the signal is removed. In the DC position the signal is coupled directly to the vertical amplifier.

10. BAL control. This control balances the DC amplifier circuits so no vertical trace shift occurs when the gain control is rotated.

11. VOLTS/CM. Each of the nine positions of this attenuator switch is marked for the number of volts (peak-to-peak) required to produce a pattern one centimeter high on the graticule. Notice that the volts/cm calibration is accurate only when the gain control is fully clockwise, in the "cal" position.

POSITIONING SECTION:

12. VERTICAL. This control moves the trace up or down.

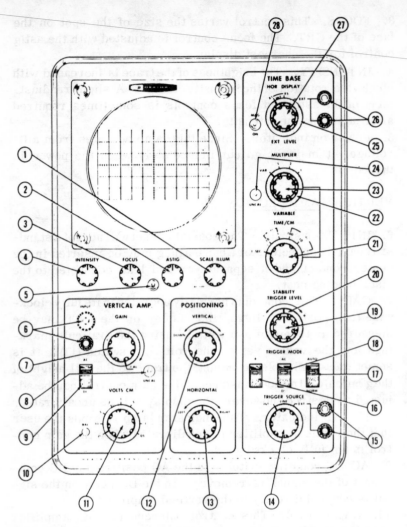

Fig. 3-13. Functions of the Heathkit Model IO-14 oscilloscope.

13. HORIZONTAL. This control moves the trace to the left or right.

TIME BASE SECTION:

14. TRIGGER SOURCE. Internal, line, or external triggering signals are selected by the trigger source switch.
15. EXT trigger input terminals. With the trigger source

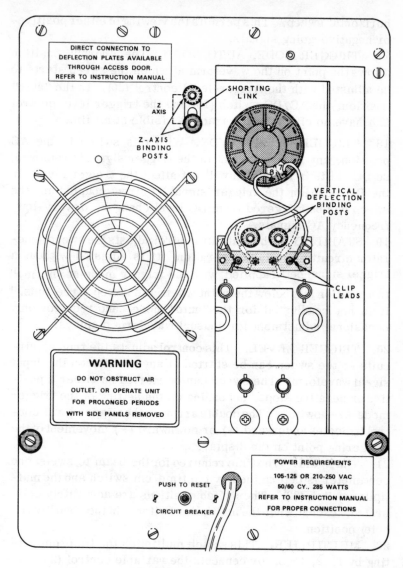

Fig. 3-14. Rear panel connections of the Heathkit Model IO-14.

switch in the "ext" position, the horizontal sweep can be triggered from an external signal applied to these binding posts.

16. TRIGGER MODE, +/−. Selects the slope of the waveform, plus (+) or minus(−), that will be used to trigger the

horizontal sweep. This permits the viewing of either positive- or negative-going signals.

17. TRIGGER MODE, AUTO/NORM. The "norm" position allows the point on the waveform at which the sweep starts to be adjusted with the trigger-level control (20). In the "auto" position, the AC/DC switch (18) and the trigger level control (20) have no effect, and a trace is visible at all times.

18. TRIGGER MODE, AC/DC. With this switch in the AC position, any DC component in the trigger signal is removed, so DC shifts in the signal will not affect the trigger level. In the DC position the trigger signal is direct coupled and the sweep can be triggered from DC level changes, or very-low-frequency AC signals.

19. STABILITY. The stability control adjusts the sweep gene- rator circuits for stable operation. It is adjusted without a trigger signal being applied, with the trigger mode at "norm," to a position just below the point where the sweep "free runs." It is not readjusted for the "auto" mode, and requires only occasional adjustment for unusual waveform displays.

20. TRIGGER LEVEL. This control adjusts the trigger cir- cuits so the sweep can be started at any position on the input signal waveform. The sweep can be started on either a posi- tive or negative slope, depending on the setting of the trigger mode + /— switch. The double arrow on the trigger level con- trol indicates an upward (+) or downward (—) movement of the triggering point on the display.

21. TIME/CM. The time required for the beam to sweep one centimeter is determined by the time/cm switch and the mul- tiplier switch (22). The switch positions are accurately cali- brated, except when the multiplier switch is in the "var"(vari- able) position.

22. MULTIPLIER. This switch multiplies the time/cm set- ting by 1, 2, or 5, or connects the variable control (23) into the circuit.

23. VARIABLE. This control is used with the time/cm switch (21) to provide a continuous adjustment of sweep time. The time base is uncalibrated when the multiplier is in the "var" position.

24. UNCAL indicator. This neon lamp glows when the mul- tiplier switch is in the "var" position, showing that the hori- zontal sweep (time base) is uncalibrated.

64

25. HOR DISPLAY switch. The normal internal sweep is seen when this switch is in the X1 position. In the X5 (magnifier) position, the waveform is 5 times longer than in the X1 position. Thus, the time/cm figure must be divided by 5. Also, with the magnifier on, the intensity of the display is reduced because the beam strikes the tube face only 1/5 of the normal time. The "ext" position couples the "hor display ext" terminals into the circuit.

26. HOR DISPLAY EXT terminals. These binding posts permit an external signal to be applied to the horizontal amplifier.

27. EXT LEVEL. This control adjusts the length of the trace when an external signal is being used.

28. MAG ON indicator. This neon lamp glows when the "hor display" switch is in the X5 position, reminding the user that the magnifier is on, and that the sweep time must be divided by 5 when making time measurements.

REAR PANEL CONNECTIONS: (Refer to Fig. 3-14)

Z-AXIS input: With the shorting link removed, a signal can be coupled to these posts to intensity-modulate the CRT electron beam. The brightness of the beam will increase when a negative pulse is applied.

DIRECT CONNECTION TO THE VERTICAL DEFLECTION PLATES:

A signal can be applied directly to the CRT vertical deflection plates by connecting it to the two red binding posts inside the rear access door. The two clip leads, normally on the outer pins of the 4-pin terminal strip, are moved to the two center pins to couple directly to the plates. NOTE: Avoid major changes in the position of these leads with respect to each other and the chassis or the AC delay line coils may require readjustment when normal conditions are restored.

TIME/CM-TO-FREQUENCY CORRELATION:

Use the following formula to determine the frequency of a waveform displayed on the CRT (1 millisecond = .001 second):

Time/cm switch setting in seconds per cm	X	Multiplier switch setting*	X	Number of centimeters on CRT for 1 cycle of the unknown frequency	=	Period of unknown waveform.

$$\frac{1}{\text{Period of unknown waveform}} = \text{Frequency of unknown waveform}$$

*NOTE: The "var" setting of this switch cannot be used in this equation since there are no calibrated values associated with the "variable" control.

EXAMPLE: .001 X 2 X 5 = .01 second

1 m sec Time/cm switch setting in seconds per cm	X	2 Multiplier switch setting	X	5 Number of centimeters on CRT for 1 cycle of the unknown frequency	=	.01 second Period of unknown waveform.

$$\frac{1}{.01} = 100 \text{ cps}$$

OPERATIONAL EXAMPLE:

The following example will help you become more familiar with the control functions, especially the sweep and trigger controls:

Connect a sine-wave source of any frequency from 10 Hz to 2 MHz to the vertical input connector. Set the trigger source switch to "int," and the trigger mode switches to (+), AC, and "norm."

Set the trigger level control all the way to either end of its rotation, and turn the stability control fully clockwise, When a trace appears on the screen, slowly turn the stability control counterclockwise until the trace just disappears; the stability control should remain in that position, because it will seldom need adjustment. Do not try to use this control to stabilize the trace or sync. If the stability control is ever

66

adjusted for a complex or unusual waveform, it should be readjusted by following the instructions here.

Now turn the trigger level control to about the center of its rotation, where the trace should reappear. Adjust the volt/cm switch to obtain a trace 3 or 4 centimeters high. Adjust the horizontal positioning control so the left edge of the trace is just inside the left margin of the graticule. Set the time/cm switch to display only a few cycles of the waveform. Adjust the vertical positioning control to center the trace vertically. Now carefully readjust the trigger level control and observe how the left edge (starting point) of the sweep moves upward as the control is turned clockwise and downward as the control is turned counterclockwise. See A in Fig. 3-15. Switch the trigger mode + /— switch to the (—) position, and notice that the trigger level control has the same effect except that the sweep start point is on the negative slope of the waveform.

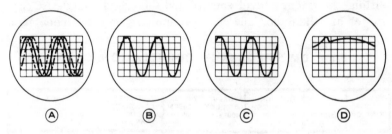

Fig. 3-15. Waveforms showing triggering level settings. (D is a magnified spike waveform).

There is no fixed rule for setting the trigger level control, as no two waveforms are alike. For example, assume that you want to examine the spike on waveform B in Fig. 3-15. By adjusting the trigger level control so the sweep starts just before the spike, as in C in Fig. 3-15, and decreasing the time required for one complete sweep by changing the position of the time/cm and/or multiplier switches, the spike can be spread out across a large area of the screen for closer observation. The spike can also be enlarged by turning the "hor display" switch to X5. The spike will then be magnified as it is in D of Fig. 3-15. By reading the time/cm and multiplier switch settings, the duration of the spike can be determined. This feature is also useful while observing distortion in circuits using square-wave signals.

The time/cm and multiplier switches should be set to display the desired waveform or portion of the waveform. Occasionally it also may be necessary to use the "var multiplier." However, the sweep time cannot be calibrated when the "var multiplier" is used. (Refer to the previous equation or the time/cm frequency Correlation Chart to determine unknown frequencies or sweep times when the calibrated positions of the time/cm and multiplier switches are used.

The trigger source switch permits you to choose between internal, line, or external triggering signals. The "int" trigger uses a portion of the vertical input signal. "Line" triggering uses a 50/60-Hz power line sample to trigger the sweep. The "ext" trigger position allows the sweep to be triggered from external sources, such as TV horizontal or vertical sync pulses, that are not necessarily related to the vertical input signal.

When the trigger mode auto/norm switch is in the "auto" position, the trigger level control and the trigger mode AC/DC switch are disabled, and a sweep appears on the screen even

TIME/CM FREQUENCY CORRELATION CHART

TIME/CM SWITCH	MULTI-PLIER	TIME FOR 1 CM SWEEP (HOR. DISPLAY X1)	FREQUENCY (CPS) FOR 1 CYCLE/10CM (full screen width)	TIME FOR 1 CM SWEEP (HOR DISPLAY X5)	FREQUENCY (CPS) FOR 1 CYCLE/10 CM (full screen width)
1 μ sec	X1	1 μ sec	100,000	.2 μ sec	500,000
1 μ sec	X2	2 μ sec	50,000	.4 μ sec	250,000
1 μ sec	X5	5 μ sec	20,000	1 μ sec	100,000
10 μ sec	X1	10 μ sec	10,000	2 μ sec	50,000
10 μ sec	X2	20 μ sec	5,000	4 μ sec	25,000
10 μ sec	X5	50 μ sec	2,000	10 μ sec	10,000
100 μ sec	X1	100 μ sec	1,000	20 μ sec	5,000
100 μ sec	X2	200 μ sec	500	40 μ sec	2,500
100 μ sec	X5	500 μ sec	200	100 μ sec	1,000
1 m sec	X1	1 m sec	100	200 μ sec	500
1 m sec	X2	2 m sec	50	400 μ sec	250
1 m sec	X5	5 m sec	20	1 m sec	100
10 m sec	X1	10 m sec	10	2 m sec	50
10 m sec	X2	20 m sec	5	4 m sec	25
10 m sec	X5	50 m sec	2	10 m sec	10
.1 sec	X1	.1 sec	1	20 m sec	5
.1 sec	X2	.2 sec	.5	40 m sec	2.5
.1 sec	X5	.5 sec	.2	.1 sec	1

in the absence of a signal. The "auto" position is useful for simple waveforms with frequencies from about 100 Hz to 2 MHz. This switch position is also useful for signals that are too weak to trigger the sweep circuits in the normal position. The trigger mode AC/DC switch will normally be in the AC position, except when using very-low-frequency or DC signals as a trigger source.

Applying A Test Signal

You need to observe some precautions in connecting the oscilloscope to the source from which signal measurements are to be made.

• False readings can be avoided, due to stray electric or magnetic coupling between circuits, particularly in the probe lead connected to the input connector of the scope. Generally, unshielded leads of appreciable length are unsuited for this use, even for the audio-frequency range, except when making checks in low-impedance circuits at very low frequencies. When shielded leads are used, the cable shields should be grounded to the oscilloscope chassis and to the chassis of the equipment under test. Coaxial cables are a must for these purposes.

• In broadband applications, it may be necessary to terminate the coaxial cable with a resistor or an attenuating pad to prevent resonance effects or ringing (high-frequency damped oscillation). It becomes more necessary to terminate the cable properly as its length is increased. This termination is normally placed at the scope input of the cable, although some test setups require additional termination at the source input of the cable. The trick is to try and simulate actual operating conditions of the equipment being tested. The equipment under test should work into a load impedance that it will see when in actual use.

• The effect of scope loading on the signal source must be considered. The input circuit can be represented by a resistance shunted by a capacitance. However, with a few feet of cable in the input circuit the loading capacitance on the circuit under investigation could be as high as 100 mmfd or more. In some cases, the effect of these resistive and capacitive loads are not negligible; therefore, a probe is needed.

Input Circuit Loading

When a scope is connected to a circuit the amplitude or waveform at the test point may be altered. To avoid this condition, the impedance of the circuit being measured must be a small fraction of the oscilloscope input impedance, since the ratio of these two impedances represents the amount of probable error. As an example, a ratio of 1 to 100 will account for about a 1% error; a ratio of 1 to 10, about a 9% error. And remember that the input impedance is not the same at all frequencies but continues to diminish at higher frequencies due to input capacitance. Even at audio frequencies this may be significant when using a shielded cable; the additional capacitance of the cable must be considered when not properly terminated.

Passive attenuator probes are used to reduce circuit loading at a sacrifice of overall sensitivity. The reduction of resistive loading due to passive probes may be as much as the attenuation ratio of the probe, but capacitive loading will not be reduced to the same extent because of the added capacitance of the probe cable. A typical 5-to-1 attenuator probe may be able to reduce capacitive loading somewhat better than 2 to 1, while a 50-to-1 attenuator probe may reduce capacitive loading by about 10 to 1. After this point very little improvement is made because of the stray capacitance introduced by the probe tip. Cathode-follower probes (or cathode-anode-follower probes) have good fast-response characteristics and do not impose great losses of signal amplitude. One way to check if a particular connection is disturbing a circuit is to attach and then detach another connection of the same type and observe any difference in the oscilloscope waveform display.

The Scope Probe and Its Uses

An attenuator probe lessens both capacitive and resistive loading and reduces sensitivity. The attenuation introduced by the probe permits measurement of signal voltages with larger amplitudes than can be measured by the preamplifier alone. When making amplitude measurements with an attenuator probe, be sure to multiply the observed amplitude by the attenuation ratio (as marked on the probe). Most oscilloscope probes have an attenuation ratio of 10 to 1, and a maximum of 600 volts that may be applied to the probe. Voltages greater than this value (either DC or peak AC volts) may damage the components inside the probe body.

HV Capacitive Divider Probe

For higher peak-to-peak voltage measurements with the scope, use a high-voltage (capacitive type) divider probe. Many times it is desirable to measure peak pulse voltages of 2,000 volts or more. A special probe has been developed for measuring high AC peak voltages in TV sweep sections. As shown in Fig. 3-16 the probe contains two capacitors; C1 is a low-capacitance, high-voltage type and C2 is a high-capacity, low-voltage type. The two capacitors in series act as a voltage divider, with the largest voltage drop appearing

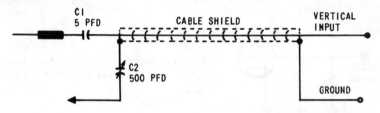

Fig. 3.16. Schematic of a HV divider probe.

across C1. Therefore, the voltage waveform that appears across C2 can be viewed on the scope (voltage from this point to ground are well within the scope's input range). Capacitor C2 is usually made adjustable so the attenuation ratio can be properly set and calibrated. A ratio of 100 to 1 is common for this type probe, again simplifying scope calibration. The HV probe will distort the 60-Hz vertical frequency and its attenuation factor is too great for use in low-signal level circuits. This probe's main purpose is for waveform measurements in horizontal output and pulse regulator plate circuits. Since the pulse at the HV rectifier plate exceeds this probe's rating, it cannot be used at this point.

Proper Probe Use

The proper use of probes is very important when reliable

measurements are to be made. Here are some of the more common considerations:

1. A probe is used primarily to reduce resistive and capacitive circuit loading.

2. Long probe leads should be restricted to the measurement of slower-changing signal information; the same goes for long ground leads.

3. The ground lead should be connected to a point where no hum or high-frequency signal components exist in the ground path between that point and the signal pick-off point. Chassis currents must be considered, also.

4. A 10-ohm resistor at the tip of a probe may prevent ringing when the probe is connected to very-low-impedance signal sources having a very-high-frequency component.

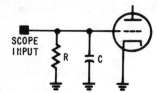

Fig. 3-17. Input circuit of a typical oscilloscope vertical deflection amplifier.

5. Resistive loading may be eliminated entirely by the use of a small (.002 mfd or larger) capacitor in series with the probe tip, at the sacrifice of some low-frequency response.

6. Avoid applying more than the rated peak voltage to a probe. Use of a high-voltage coupling capacitor between a probe tip and a very high DC level may not always prevent probe burnout, since the capacitor must charge through the probe. However, if care is taken to charge and discharge the blocking capacitor through a path which shunts the probe, this technique can be a successful one. A recommended procedure is to permanently attach the blocking capacitor to the probe tips and ground the junction of the capacitor and tip whenever the capacitor is being charged or discharged.

7. Check for proper probe compensation whenever changing a probe or when making an important measurement.

Connecting the Probe to the Scope

The vertical amplifier input circuit can be simulated by a high resistance (R) shorted by a small shunt capacitance (C) in Fig. 3-17. In some applications even this high resistance and small capacitance can produce undesirable loading upon the circuit whose waveforms are being checked. This loading can cause scope presentations to be different from the waveforms that would be seen if the oscilloscope was disconnected. One use of a passive probe is to reduce this resistive-capacitive loading on the circuit under test.

Low-Capacitance Probe

A low-C probe includes a resistor (Rp) shunted by a capaci-

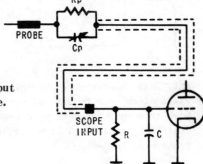

Fig. 3-18. Scope vertical input circuit using a passive probe.

tor (Cp) in Fig. 3-18. This combination is connected in series with the inner cable conductor to the scope input. As a result, when the probe is connected to the circuit under study, there is connected to that circuit a new effective loading capacitance smaller than the original capacitance C and a new effective loading resistance larger than the original resistance R. Thus the loading effect of the oscilloscope input circuit on the circuit under test is reduced through use of the probe. The probe is marked with the new effective shunt resistance and capacitance placed across the circuit under investigation when the probe is used.

A second effect of the probe is to reduce the amount of signal voltage applied directly to the oscilloscope input connection for a given amount of original signal voltage. This re-

duction occurs because of the voltage-divider action of Rp and
R. This effect is taken into account in the attenuation ratio
marked on the probe. Thus, if the probe is marked "10x
atten" you have to multiply all oscilloscope voltages measured
by 10.

Now suppose we are using a scope equipped with a probe to
look at a square-wave signal. If probe capacitor Cp were
absent, or if Cp were too small, some of the high-frequency
components of the square wave would be bypassed around the
oscilloscope input terminals by input capacitance C. Thus,
the steepness of the leading edge of the displayed square wave
would be reduced. Notice Fig. 3-19A. If probe capacitor Cp
is adjusted to the correct value, a compensating amount of
high-frequency information will be bypassed around probe resistor Rp to make up for the loss through C, and the leading

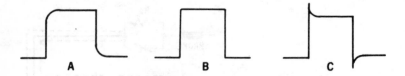

Fig. 3-19. Square wave showing: (A) effect of high-frequency
attenuation as a result of probe misalignment; (B) optimum
high-frequency response as a result of correct probe adjustment; (C) accentuated high-frequency response as a result of
probe misalignment.

edge of the displayed square wave will be like its original
shape, as seen in Fig. 3-19B. However, if Cp is too large,
the high-frequency response of the circuit will be over-com-
pensated and too much high-frequency information will be fed
to the input of the oscilloscope. This will result in overshoot
display (Fig. 3-19C) that was not present in the original signal. By adjusting Cp to its correct value, while using the
probe to display the square wave generated by the voltage
calibrator found on most professional scopes, adjust for the
flattest top, as shown in Fig. 3-19B. Serious errors might
be introduced into your observations if you do not check this
adjustment regularly. In particular, the probe adjustment
must be checked whenever you use it with an oscilloscope or
a plug-in preamplifier whose input capacitance is different
from that of the instrument with which the probe was pre-
viously used.

74

Demodulator Probe

For observations of TV, RF, or IF signals a detector type probe is needed. You will use this type probe for signal tracing or sensitivity and stage-gain measurements. The RF probe makes the wideband oscilloscope a fine instrument for observation of a reasonably exact waveshape of the high-frequency signal at these test points. The two principal characteristics of this probe are: a low capacitance that will not detune or load down the circuit under test, and a detector or demodulator to convert the high-frequency signal to video or audio as in the case of a modulated signal or to DC as with a pure RF carrier signal. A crystal detector of silicon or germanium is used because of its good response at low signal levels. The leads for this probe need to be short in order to keep the capacitance low.

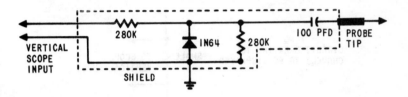

Fig. 3-20. Schematic of a crystal detector probe.

Shown in Fig. 3-20 is a circuit for an RF demodulator probe. An input blocking capacitor and an output isolation resistor are used in order to keep the circuit under test as undisturbed as possible. Signal checks with this type of probe can be made in almost any RF or IF circuit. An RF signal generator can be used to inject a signal into the stage under test, while the scope and detector probe are used to evaluate the output signal. Overall stage gain of the whole RF or IF amplifier system may be determined also in this manner. This same probe can be used for TV alignment adjustments.

Caution: Often the point being measured with this probe may by necessity have a small capacitance in series with the signal. With the probe test point in series with such a capacitance a reduction in measured signal level will occur because of the voltage-divider action between the series capacitor and the one in the probe itself. Allow for such a reduction is estimating or evaluating these results.

You may find a need at times to observe a varying current, rather than a varying voltage. However, the oscilloscope vertical-deflection amplifier is basically a voltage-sensitive device. One way of displaying a varying current is to insert a small value resistor (Fig. 3-21) in series with the circuit carrying the current we want to see. The varying current in the circuit produces a signal voltage drop across R. The waveform of the voltage across R will correspond to the original current waveform. Thus, when we display the waveform of the signal voltage drop across R in Fig. 3-21, in effect we display the current waveform found in the original circuit.

Sometimes it isn't practical to use the series-resistance method just discussed. For example, we might find it diffi-

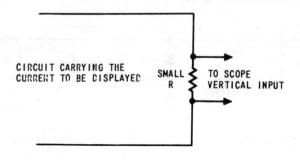

Fig. 3-21. Schematic of a "current" probe.

cult (or even impossible) to insert a series resistor, or you might want to display the currents in many different circuits. In that case the job of inserting series resistors would require too much time, or a small resistance may disturb the circuit under test too much. This, then, calls for a current probe. A current probe includes a U-shaped core of magnetic material. The U-shaped core is slipped over the conductor whose current is to be measured. The magnetic circuit is completed by sliding a bar of magnetic material over the U, in effect creating a transformer. The circuit under test is a one-turn "primary winding," and the probe itself is a secondary winding on the U-shaped core. The secondary voltage that results from a "primary" current change drives the probe cable. The output of the probe cable can be connected to either a passive termination block or to the scope's vertical input circuit.

CHAPTER 4

Looking Behind The Front Panel

Since a cathode-ray oscilloscope is an instrument designed for analysis of voltage and current waveforms, it may be used to study any variable, within the limits of its frequency response characteristics, which can be converted into electrical potentials.

Operation

The basic elements of an oscilloscope are the CRT, linear time-base generator, vertical deflection amplifier, delay line, horizontal deflection amplifier, and power supply. The display on the face of the CRT is a visual presentation of a varying voltage or current with respect to time. For a graphical explanation of this function refer to Fig. 4-1. The sawtooth waveform is applied to the horizontal deflection plates where it influences the path followed by the electron beam.

The sawtooth voltage is generated by a linear time-base generator, and this voltage, or some other desired external voltage, is used for horizontal deflection. This sawtooth voltage (or external voltage) is then fed into the horizontal deflection amplifier which increases the amplitude to that needed for a trace of the desired length. The variable voltage to be observed is applied to the vertical signal input terminals and is amplified to the desired level before being applied to the vertical deflection plates.

Fig. 4-1 shows how a sine wave is reproduced on the face of the CRT when a sawtooth voltage is applied to the horizontal plates and a sine-wave voltage to the vertical plates.

The result is a single-cycle sine wave on the screen—providing that the duration of one cycle of sawtooth voltage is the same as one cycle of sine-wave voltage. To display two cycles of the sine wave on the screen the period of the sawtooth voltage must be twice that of the sine wave; that is, its frequency must be one-half of the sine-wave frequency.

A block diagram of a typical oscilloscope is shown in Fig. 4-2. The functions and controls are graphically represented by the circle and pointer. These controls are external adjustments and are necessary for proper use of the scope.

Starting with the vertical input, the signal to be displayed enters the scope and is terminated in a precision attenuator, controlled by the external adjustment labeled "vertical gain." After passing the attenuator, the signal enters the vertical

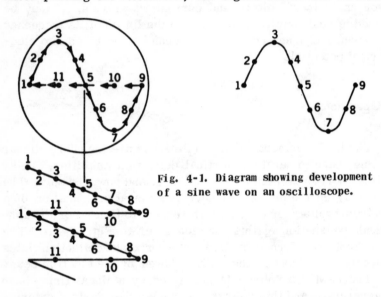

Fig. 4-1. Diagram showing development of a sine wave on an oscilloscope.

amplifier, which is usually a constant - gain device so that only the attenuator determines the calibration of the signal displayed on the screen of the CRT. The output of the vertical amplifier follows two paths. The first path is to the vertical deflection amplifier where the signal is amplified sufficiently to produce a proportional DC variation with respect to the input signal. The vertical centering control adds or subtracts a constant DC potential to the vertical deflection plates to allow for vertical centering of the sweep display. The second path leads to a switch which selects either internal or external synchronization. On internal synchronization, the time-base oscillator is adjusted so as to be very close in frequency relationship with the signal. Consequently, the test signal will control the time-base oscillator. When this function is accomplished, a steady display of the signal will appear on the CRT.

The time-base oscillator output, now synchronized with the vertical input signal, goes to the sawtooth shaper which creates a linear-rise-time voltage used to drive the horizontal deflection amplifier. Connected to the horizontal deflection amplifier is an internal and external sweep switch. At this point we may use the linear time base synchronized sawtooth voltage or select an external sweep signal. The horizontal deflection amplifier and the horizontal centering control function the same as the vertical deflection and centering circuits, with the one exception that the horizontal deflection plates are now being excited. The horizontal blanking amplifier is used in conjunction with the horizontal sweep circuits. It controls the intensity of the display during retrace time so as to darken (blank out) the display during the interval of time it takes for the beam to return to its initial starting place.

Shown in Fig. 4-3 is a block diagram of another typical professional oscilloscope (omitting the power supply section). The waveform (1) to be observed is fed into the vertical amplifier input. The calibrated volts/div. control sets the gain of this amplifier. The push-pull output (3 and 4) of the vertical amplifier is fed through a delay line to the vertical-deflection plates of the CRT. (The purpose of the delay line is explained later in this Chapter.)

The time-base generator or "sweep generator" develops a sawtooth wave (12) that is used as a horizontal-deflection voltage. The rising or positive-going part of the sawtooth, called the "run-up" portion of the wave, is linear; that is, the waveform rises through a given number of volts during each unit of time. This rate of rise is set by the calibrated time /div. control. The sawtooth voltage is fed to the time-base amplifier, which includes a phase inverter so that the amplifier supplies two output sawtooth waveforms (15 and 16) simultaneously—one of them positive-going, like the input, and the other negative-going. The positive-going sawtooth is applied to the right-hand horizontal deflection plate of the cathode-ray tube, and the negative-going sawtooth is applied

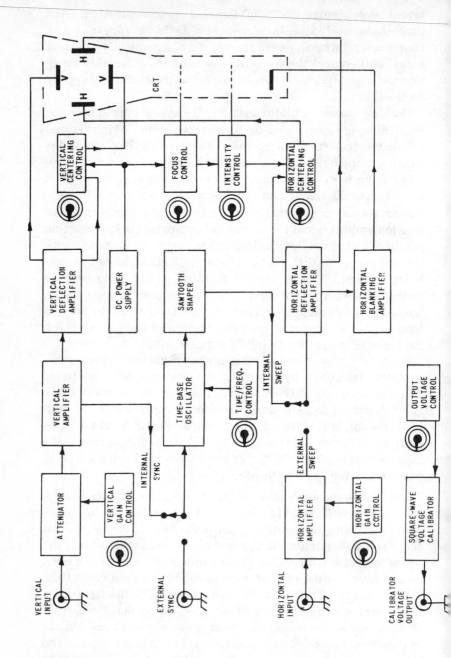

Fig. 4-2. Block diagram of a typical oscilloscope.

to the left-hand deflection plate. As a result, the cathode-ray beam is swept horizontally to the right through a given number of graticule divisions during each unit of time; the sweep rate is controlled by the time/div. control.

In order to maintain a stable display on the CRT screen, each horizontal sweep must start at the same point on the waveform being displayed. Therefore, a sample of the displayed waveform is fed to a "trigger" circuit that gives a negative output voltage spike (7) at some selected point on the display waveform. This triggering spike is used to start the run-up portion of the time-base sawtooth generator. As far as the display is concerned, then, "triggering" can be taken as synonymous with the starting of the horizontal sweep of the trace at the left-hand side of the graticule.

A rectangular "unblanking" wave (9) derived from the time-base generator is applied to the grid of the CRT. The duration of the positive part of this rectangular wave corresponds to the duration of the positive-going or run-up part of the time-base output, so that the beam is switched on during its left-to-right travel and is switched off during its right-to-left retrace. Of course, it takes a measurable time for the trigger to start the horizontal sweep. As shown in the lower section of Fig. 4-3 an interval on the order of 0.1 microsecond is required to begin the trace. Furthermore, the time-base generator also generates the unblanking waveform that turns on the CRT beam, so there isn't even any spot on the screen until the unavoidable delay interval has elapsed and the time-base generator is activated. Thus, there is a waiting interval while the time-base generator gets the horizontal sweep started and the cathode-ray-tube spot unblanked. And during this wait the early part of the displayed waveform (its leading edge) might be partly or entirely over with.

To make it possible to see the entire displayed waveform, including the leading edge, a delay of about 0.25 microsecond is introduced between the vertical-amplifier output and the CRT vertical deflection plates. The delay line holds back or delays the test waveform from the vertical delfection plates until the time-base generator has time to get the horizontal sweep in action and have the CRT beam unblanked. Thus, we then have a chance to see the leading edge of the displayed waveform. The delay line may be a simple coiled length of

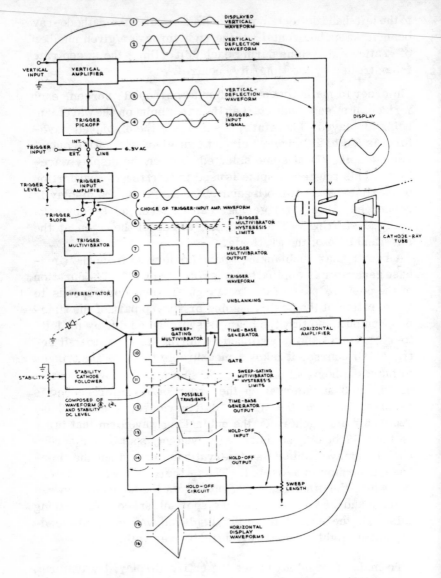

Fig. 4-3. Block diagram of a typical professional oscilloscope.

coaxial cable or a coiled length of wire wound on a tube, somewhat like that found in the color TV receiver chassis.

To summarize the purpose of the delay line, it is to retard the application of the observed waveform to the vertical deflection plates until the trigger and time-base circuits have had an opportunity to initiate unblanking and horizontal sweep

82

operations. In this way, we can view the entire desired waveform even though the leading edge of that waveform was used to trigger the horizontal sweep.

Horizontal Deflection System

The time-base trigger develops a pulse which starts a cycle of action in the time-base generator. The trigger slope switch allows the operator to select the "slope," either positive or negative, which will trigger the sweep.

Trigger Input Amplifier

Using an internal source of triggering signal, either triggered operation in the various triggering modes or synchronized operation can be used. Fig. 4-4 shows a simplified trigger circuit. Triggered or synchronized operation may be produced from an external source. Operation in any one of the available modes is possible with external signals, also.

Trigger Multivibrator

The trigger oscillator is a DC - coupled multivibrator. In the quiescent state (ready to receive a signal), V45A (Fig. 4-4) is conducting and the plate voltage is down. Since the plate is DC - coupled to the grid of V45B, that grid is held below cutoff. With V45B cut off, its plate voltage is up and no output will develop. The negative - going portion of the signal from the trigger-input amplifier is required to drive the grid of V45A down. As the V45A grid is driven negative, the current flow through the tube is restricted and the voltage at the plate starts to rise. The rise in voltage at the plate then carries the grid in the positive direction. The trigger multivibrator produces a square wave which is coupled to the time-base generator. This square wave is differentiated in the time-base generator to produce a sharp, negative-going pulse which is used to trigger the time-base generator in the proper time sequence when triggered operation is desired.

Sweep Trigger and Sync

The sweep generator in a service scope runs continuously, and to present a steady display the generator is run at a fre-

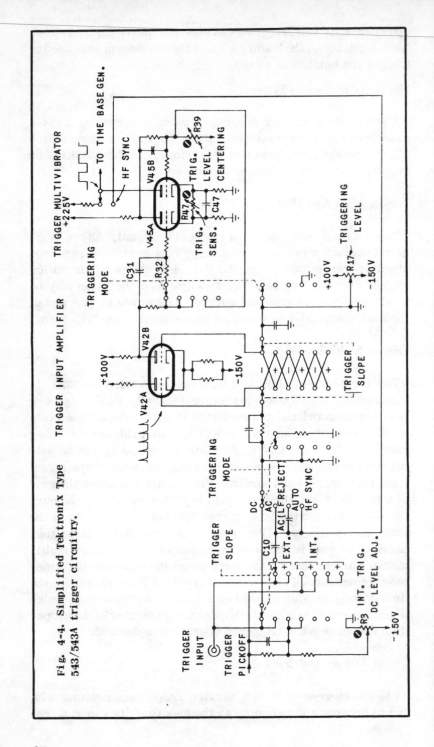

Fig. 4-4. Simplified Tektronix Type 543/543A trigger circuitry.

quency that is equal to (or a multiple of) the signal being displayed. This process is called synchronizing and is achieved by applying a suitable sample of the signal to the sweep generator. That system is limited to displaying recurrent signals which do not vary in amplitude or frequency and which have little or no "dead time" between waveforms. A more direct system is necessary to display pulses of short duration and low repetition rate, where the pulses themselves "drive" or "trigger" the sweeps; hence, the development of the triggered-sweep scope. We now commonly trigger sweeps by generating a triggering pulse internally from whatever triggering waveform is selected. This method accommodates almost any type of triggering signal except those having a very high frequency. For this reason the early synchronizing method is often included in modern scopes. It should be noted that this synchronizing method is very difficult or impossible to achieve if the synchronizing signal varies in amplitude or frequency.

Triggering Level and Scope Selection

Often it is necessary to prevent sweeps from being triggered by extraneous, undesired low-amplitude signals (like a type of noise). Therefore, most scopes incorporate a triggering level control which determines the minimum triggering sensitivity. Then, if a noise pulse comes along it has to be strong enough to get past the triggering level control, which incidentally, provides a selection of either positive or negative voltage levels. And because the triggering signal may possess either a positive or negative slope, a plus or minus slope selector is also found on these scopes. These two controls offer an additional feature which is often very advantageous—that of "ranging" or "phasing." By this means triggering may be held off deliberately for long periods. The display of a sine wave may be displaced horizontally (phased) by triggering at different levels on either of its two slopes.

Automatic Triggering

Many signals displayed on a scope are simple in structure; that is, they are alike from one cycle to the next and occur at regular intervals. Many such signals can be displayed without any "knob twisting" of the triggering controls if the scope

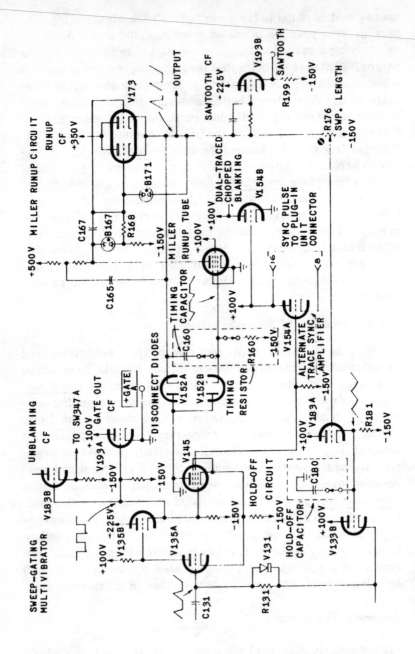

Fig. 4-5. Simplified Tektronix Type 543/543A time-base circuitry.

is provided with an automatic triggering mode. If the time-base generator is anywhere near the correct sweep speed the scope will automatically lock the waveshape rock steady on the CRT. This is a handy feature for vertical and horizontal TV pulse checks and even will lock in a sine-wave signal, which can be a tough task for some scopes.

Triggering Sensitivity

Triggering sensitivity is the most significant factor governing the display of the leading edge of a signal when triggering slowly rising waveforms. For instance, if the scope is capable of triggering signals which are so small that they cover only 4% of the full vertical scale, it should be possible to display all but approximately 4% of the leading edge of signals which occupy the full vertical scale. The triggering sensitivity consideration is important when separate externally applied signals are to be observed, if such signals are small.

Sweep Speed Range

Whatever the total sweep speed range may be, continuous coverage usually is provided. The sweep range on most scopes is calibrated in discrete steps, like those of a voltmeter. A variable sweep-time/division control also may be provided to offer continuous coverage between steps and it may or may not be calibrated. Such a variable control is convenient when we want to spread or compress a display to let some portion of the waveform cover a particular number of divisions, as in phase comparisons or measurements. If calibrated, the variable control allows fractional time measurements to be made without using subdivisions of the scale. Unless the variable control is calibrated, a scope should have each stepped change in sweep-time/division represent a small change ratio. This arrangement permits any time measurement to be made over a large portion of the horizontal scale, except (possibly) when using the fastest sweep. Today we commonly use the step frequency 1, 2, 5, 10, 20, 50, and so on.

Time Base Accuracy

Time-base accuracy is usually specified in terms of the

permissible full-scale sweep timing error for any calibrated sweep; that is, an accuracy of 3% means that the actual full-scale period of any sweep should not be more than 3% greater or less than indicated. Magnified sweeps may have poorer accuracy ratings than unmagnified sweeps, since magnification is usually achieved by reducing amplifier feedback.

Sweep linearity is an important factor which is seldom specified. There are various forms of sweep nonlinearity and several types may exist all in one scope. Because of this, there seems to be no simple way to specify linearity in terms which are significant in all cases without implying that the sweeps in general are worse than they are. Experience or judicious side-by-side comparison is needed here. The fastest sweeps are usually the most nonlinear, with the most prevalent kind of nonlinearity being slowness at the beginning and end of the sweep.

Time Base Generator

The trigger circuit produces a negative-going waveform which is coupled to the time-base generator. See Fig. 4-5. This waveform is differentiated in the grid circuit of V135A to produce a sharp negative-going pulse to trigger the time-base generator in the proper time sequence. The time-base generator consists of three main circuits; a sweep-gating multivibrator, a Miller run-up circuit, and a hold-off circuit. The sweep-gating multivibrator consists of V135A, V145, and cathode follower V135B. The essential components of the Miller run-up circuit are the Miller tube V161, the run-up C.F. V173, the on-off diodes V152, timing capacitor C160, and timing resistor R160. The hold-off circuit consists of hold-off C.F. V183A-V133B, hold-off capacitor C180, and resistor R181.

Miller Run-Up Circuit

The quiescent state of the Miller circuit is determined by a DC network between plate and grid (Fig. 4-5). This network consists of neon glow tube B167, run-up C.F. V173, and on-off diodes V152. The purpose of this network is to establish a voltage of such a value at the plate of the Miller tube that it (tube) will operate above the knee (over the linear region)

88

of its characteristic curve. This quiescent plate voltage is about 43 volts.

Sweep Generation

If the stability and triggering level controls are adjusted for triggered operation, a negative pulse will drive the grid of V135A below cutoff and force the sweep-gating multivibrator into its other state in which V145 is the conducting tube. As V145 conducts its plate drops, cutting off the on - off diodes, V152. Any spiking that may occur during this transition is attenuated by the C150-R150 network (Fig. 4-6).

With V152 cut off, the grid of the Miller tube and the cathode of the run-up C.F. are free to seek their own voltages. The grid of the Miller tube then starts to drop, since it is connected to the -150-volt bus through timing resistor R160. The plate voltage of the Miller tube starts to rise, carrying with it the grid and cathode of V173. This raises the voltage at the top of timing capacitor C160, which in turn pulls up the grid of the Miller tube and prevents it from dropping. The gain of the Miller tube (as a Class A amplifier) is so high that the voltage coupled back through C160 keeps the grid voltage constant within a fraction of a volt.

The timing capacitor then starts charging from the -150-volt bus. The charging current flows through timing resistor R160. Since the voltage at the grid of the Miller tube remains essentially constant, the voltage drop across the timing resistor remains essentially constant, providing a constant source of charging current for C160. By this action C160 charges linearly, and the voltage at the cathode of V173 rises linearly. Any departure from a linear rise in voltage at this point will produce a change in the voltage at the grid of the Miller tube in a direction to correct for the error. Fig. 4-6 is a complete diagram of a professional scope horizontal-deflection system.

Hold-Off

The hold-off circuit prevents the time-base generator from being triggered during the retrace interval. You might say the hold-off allows a finite time for the time-base circuits to regain a state of equilibrium after the completion of a sweep.

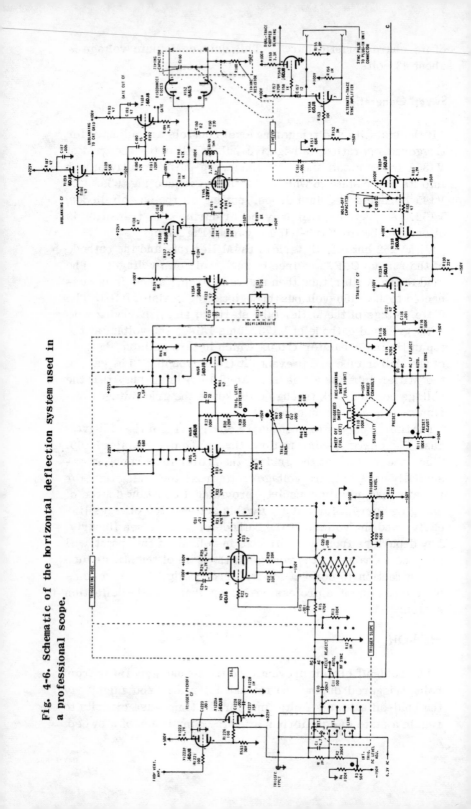

Fig. 4-6. Schematic of the horizontal deflection system used in a professional scope.

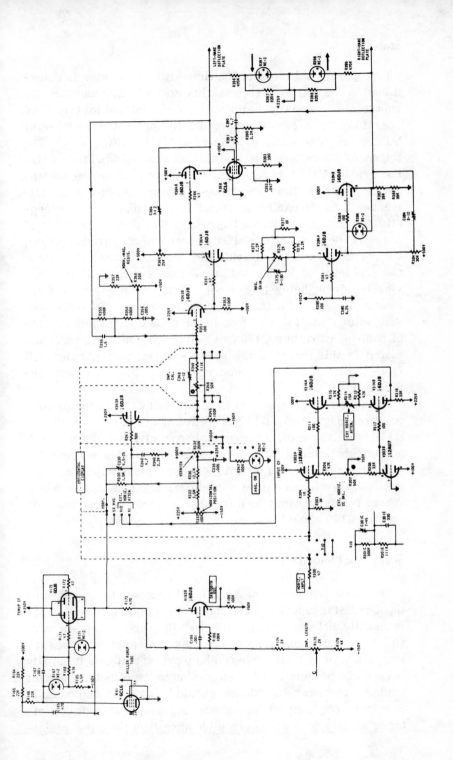

Stability

The operational mode of the time - base generator is determined by the setting of the stability control. By means of this
control the sweep can be turned off and adjusted for triggered
operation. The stability control, through cathode - follower
V133A, regulates the grid level of V135A (Fig. 4-6). For
triggered operation, the stability control is adjusted so that
the grid of V135A is just high enough to prevent the sweep-
gating multivibrator from free - running. Adjusted in this
manner a sweep can be produced only when an incoming negative trigger pulse drives the grid of V135A below cutoff.

Moving the arm of the stability control toward ground (CCW),
but not far enough to activate the preset switch, will raise
the grid level of V133A and prevent the sweep - gating multivibrator from being triggered. This, then, turns off the
sweep action. With the arm moved toward -150 volts, the
grid voltage of V133 will drop to the point where the discharge
of hold-off capacitor C180 can switch the multivibrator. Adjusted in this manner, the sweep - gating multivibrator will
free - run and produce a recurrent sweep like that on a service scope.

When the stability control is turned full CCW to the pre-set
position (Fig. 4-6), R110 is switched out of the circuit and
R111 is switched in. This control, a front-panel screwdriver
adjustment labeled "pre - set adjust," provides a fixed DC
voltage for the grid of V133A. When properly adjusted, pre-
set operation can be used for most triggering applications.
Where triggering may be difficult, however, manual stability
control R110 should be used.

Scope Input Impedance

The input impedance of most oscilloscopes is specified by
input resistance and input capacitance. The input resistance
is usually between about 100K and 10 meg, except in very
wideband instruments where the input resistance matches the
impedance of coaxial cables. The input capacitance is usually
between 20 pfd and 50 pfd. To minimize the effects of circuit
loading, the input impedance should be as high as possible.
For high-frequency or fast-rising signals, the input capacitance usually does more circuit loading than the input resist-

ance. For example, at 8 kHz a 20-pfd capacitor has a reactance equal to 1 meg. Thus, at higher frequencies the capacitance has more effect on loading than a 1 meg input resistance. When a coaxial cable is used between a scope input and the test point, the added capacitance of the cable further increases loading. Therefore, passive attenuator probes are used, instead of plain coaxial cables, to reduce loading effects. Such probes may attenuate loading by a factor as great as the signal attenuation they impose. At high attenuation ratios (about 10 to 1), the stray capacitance at the probe tip (about 2 pfd) becomes more prominent.

CRT Phosphors

The luminance or brightness of a CRT screen is dependent upon the phosphor and the accelerating potential. That's why, when considering this characteristic, the measurement system's acceleration potential should be stated. Many professional scopes have a 10 KV accelerating potential. When the electron beam strikes the phosphor, light and heat are emitted. The light is of primary interest, but the presence of heat and the possibility of burning the phosphor must be considered. When the CRT phosphor is excited, this phenomenon is called luminescence, while light produced after the source energy is removed is known as phosphorescence.

Build-Up Time

If a phosphor is suddenly excited by an electron beam, it requires some finite time for the light output to reach a constant level. The time required to reach 90% of that level under specified excitation conditions is called the build-up time of the phosphor. The build-up time of some phosphors is dependent upon the excitation conditions. Build-up time is appreciably shorter if the beam current density is increased.

Decay Time

When the excitation is instantly removed from a phosphor, an interval of time is required for the light output to drop to a low level. This time is known as decay time and is usually expressed as the time required for the light output to drop

below a certain percentage of the original luminance level.
The decay characteristic is sometimes called the CRT's persistence.

Phosphor Burning

When a phosphor is excited by an electron beam having an
excessively high current density, a permanent loss of phosphor efficiency may occur. The light output of the damaged
phosphor will be reduced, and in extreme cases complete
destruction of the phosphor may result. Darkening or burning
occurs when the heat developed by electron bombardment cannot be dissipated rapidly enough by the phosphor.

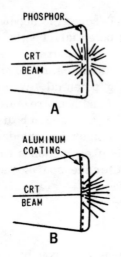

Fig. 4-7. Sketch showing the
effect of an aluminized CRT
screen.

The two most important and controllable factors affecting the
occurrence of burning are beam current density (controllable
with the intensity, focus, and astigmatism controls) and the
length of time the beam excites a given section of the phosphor
(controllable with the time/div. control). Under normal conditions the ambient voltage of the control grid will hold the
tube in cutoff and no spot will be seen on the CRT. When the
sweep is triggered and all is working properly, the beam
can be seen as it moves across the screen. However, what
if the horizontal amplifier is inoperative? Obviously, the
beam will not be deflected, but it will be turned on by the unblanking pulse. Result: Possibly a CRT screen burn! The
intensity control can be adjusted to over-ride the normal cut-

94

off condition of the gun in the absence of an unblanking pulse in a CRT using grid unblanking. If this is done, a spot of high intensity will be seen on the face of the CRT. If the sweep is now triggered, an unreasonably bright spot will occur. What happens? You guessed it—a burnt screen phosphor. So remember, burning is a function of intensity and time, and keeping intensity down or the time short will save the screen.

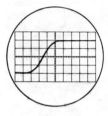

Fig. 4-8. CRT graticule gives meaning to a waveform.

Aluminized Tubes

When an electron beam excites a particle of the phosphor, light is emitted in all directions. Therefore, only part of the light emitted is seen when viewing the CRT. As shown in Fig. 4-7A, some of the light is lost as it is emitted back into the tube. To prevent this loss of light the back of the phosphor is coated with a thin layer of aluminum which acts as a mirror.

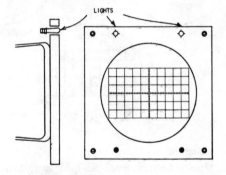

Fig. 4-9. Sketch showing the position of an external graticule.

The electron beam will penetrate the aluminum coating and the emitted light that would be lost is reflected forward as illustrated in Fig. 4-7B. Of course, some of the effective energy of the beam is used to penetrate the aluminum coating, thus reducing the effective acceleration potential. The effective deceleration of the beam depends on the thickness of the aluminum and may range from 1KV to 3KV or more. The overall result is, however, a brighter trace for an aluminized CRT.

Writing Speed

"Writing speed" expresses the maximum single-shot spot velocity (in cm/microsecond) which may be recorded on film as a just-visible trace. Where the highest possible photo-

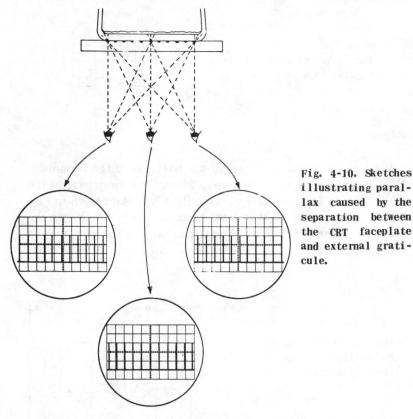

Fig. 4-10. Sketches illustrating parallax caused by the separation between the CRT faceplate and external graticule.

graphic writing rate is required, a phosphor having blue fluorescence such as P11 is generally used, since most types of film are more sensitive to blue light. Sometimes a trace may be visible to the eye in a darkened room, but difficulty may be encountered in trying to photograph the display.

Graticules

The display on the face of a CRT would be meaningless if

there were no markings to indicate divisions. In Fig. 4-8 various time and amplitude characteristics of the display may be determined by counting the number of divisions and multiplying by the appropriate switch setting.

An external graticule consists of a piece of scribed plexiglass mounted in front of the CRT as shown in Fig. 4-9. In some scopes two graticule lamps, which illuminate the scribed lines, are controlled by the scale illumination control on the scope's front panel. This type of graticule has the advantage of being easily changed. Graticules marked in degrees for color TV vector analysis, special rise-time markings, or many other patterns, may be quickly mounted on the scope.

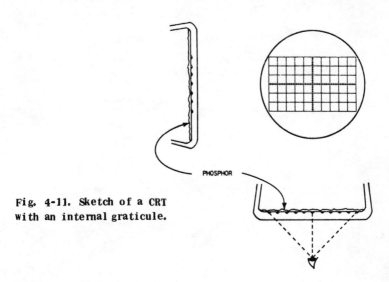

PHOSPHOR

Fig. 4-11. Sketch of a CRT with an internal graticule.

Parallax

The external graticule has the major disadvantage of introducing a condition called parallax, as shown in Fig. 4-10. The scribed lines on the graticule are on a different plane than the trace. Therefore, the alignment of the trace and the graticule will vary from different viewing positions. Visual observation parallax can be overcome by always viewing the trace at one point—at a 90° angle. Observing the trace at a second point requires moving the head to maintain the 90° angle at the new position. This will correct for parallax. A camera has similar parallax problems and cannot be shifted.

A graticule on the inside surface of the face plate of the CRT, as shown in Fig. 4-11, is called an internal graticule. The trace and the graticule are in the same plane and there is no parallax. This type of graticule is more costly to manufacture and cannot be changed without changing CRTs. Edge lighting the graticule lines is more difficult and illumination is not as bright as in an external graticule. This type of graticule also requires some means of trace alignment, which adds to the cost.

CHAPTER 5

Interpreting Waveform Displays

An oscilloscope in the hands of an unskilled operator is of little value, but put to use by a skilled technician it makes circuit troubleshooting much easier. Any oscilloscope, regardless of its capabilities, is at the mercy of its operator and waveshape displays are often misinterpreted. For instance, a perfect square wave can be viewed where one does not exist just by overloading the vertical amplifiers. And for TV-IF alignment the response curve can be made to look better than it actually is by improper adjustment of the oscilloscope controls. So it is imperative that the technician learn to interpret—accurately—the waveforms displayed on the scope.

Scope Frequency Response

The first quality sought in a scope is adequate rise time and high-frequency sine-wave response. Rise time is the more important specification for "faster" scopes, and passband (bandwidth) the more frequently used specification for "slower" scopes. The two are closely related mathematically, however, as fast step signals may produce little or no overshoot or ringing. Ideally, scopes should have a vertical system capable of rising in about one-fifth the time of the fastest applied step signal. In such a case, the rise time of the signal (as indicated on the scope) will be in error only by about 2%, assuming sweep timing and linearity are perfect. Vertical deflection systems which have a rise time no better than equal to the fastest rising signal applied are often considered adequate. Such reasoning is based on the fact that the indicated rise time will be in error by a predictable amount when transient response is optimum. Under such conditions, signal rise time can be calculated to a close approximation.

When the fastest sweep is relatively slow compared with vertical-deflection system rise time (or the scale is small to start with, measurements become confined to very small sections of the screen, and the probability of measurement errors become worse.

Transient Response

The faithfulness with which a deflection system displays fast-rising step signals is termed its transient response. The most common transient response distortions are: over-

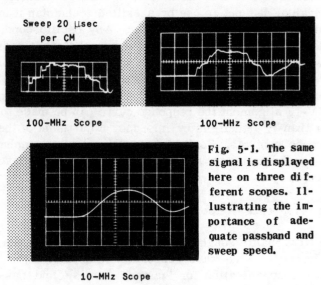

Fig. 5-1. The same signal is displayed here on three different scopes. Illustrating the importance of adequate passband and sweep speed.

shoot, ringing, and reflections from impedance discontinuities in the vertical signal delay line. These forms of distortion will make "clean" step signals appear to have spikes, squiggles, or bumps when they actually do not, and they will make "unclear" signals appear worse. Because an oscilloscope is the best instrument for evaluating step-signal waveforms, transient fidelity is essential.

Transient fidelity seldom is specified except in terms of percent of permissible overshoot. Unfortunately, transient response does not remain good indefinitely without some adjustment. One particular vacuum-tube defect is most often responsible for degradation of transient response. Known as "cathode interface," the defect shows up as excessive over-shoot after several hundred hours of use. "Interface" is due to a loss of tube gain for all but the high-frequency signal components.

Bandwidth Requirements

Important features of a displayed waveform might remain entirely concealed if the oscilloscope vertical amplifier band-width is too narrow (that is, if the vertical deflection system rise time is too long). As an example, in Fig. 5-1 are dis-plays produced by the same waveform on three different os-cilloscopes having vertical bandwidths of 10, 100, and 1,000 MHz, respectively. This example shows that a wide-band oscilloscope can reveal details that we might never see if an oscilloscope of limited bandwidth (relatively long rise time) were used.

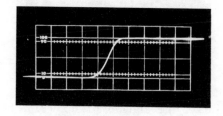

Fig. 5-2. Sweep rate of 0.1 μsec/cm shows a rise time of 0.12 μsec.

Rise Time

The merit of a wide-band amplifier is often specified by its rise time. Rise time is the time of transition between 10 and 90% of the amplitude of a step signal (Fig. 5-2). For ampli-fiers with good transient response, input-signal rise time and amplifier rise time combine to produce an output signal rise time equal to the square root of the sum of their squares. Accuracy of measurement is therefore impaired when a scope must indicate the rise time of signals which equal (or nearly equal) its amplifier rise time. The rise time of a scope amp-lifier may be measured by applying step voltages having a much shorter rise time than the amplifier and simply reading the indicated rise time. Then by using the following formula, one can make fairly accurate calculations of input-signal rise times which are nearly as fast as, or even a little faster than, the scope amplifier.

$$Ts = \sqrt{Ti^2 - Ta^2}$$

where Ts = input signal rise time, Ti = indicated rise time and Ta = amplifier rise time.

Fast Transient Response Distortion

Distortion of a fast step signal may take several forms in various combinations—overshoot, ringing, delay-line reflections, and rise-time degradation. The observation and correction of distortion depends on the use of fast, clean, step signals of known rise time connected to the oscilloscope with a properly terminated cable.

Signal leads and grounding leads must be kept short when

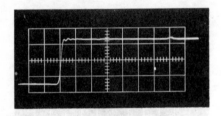

Fig. 5-3. Ringing caused by a 6-inch lead.

carrying signals having very-high-frequency components. The inductance of 4- or 5-inch leads can distort very fast changing signals. This is particularly true of very-low-impedance signal sources. The ringing in Fig. 5-3 was caused by a 6-inch lead between a 52-ohm termination and the scope input.

Probes are a possible cause of fast-transient distortion. Since most passive probes are not terminated at either end in the characteristic impedance of the cable, the resultant reflections may introduce ringing. Long probes ring at lower frequencies than short ones. In general, scopes with bandwidths of 10 MHz or less will tolerate attenuator probes as long as 4 feet without difficulty. With AC coupling the amplitude reduction of high-frequency signals of slow-response limitations is considerable, but roll-off is expected at signal frequencies near the bandwidth limits of an amplifier. Such an upper limit exists even for DC-coupled amplifiers. Excessive high-frequency peaking can extend this upper limit, of course, but it produces serious transient distortion when used in oscilloscope amplifiers. Bandwidth and rise time are closely related mathematically when transient response is optimum; the rise time is close to 35% of the time for one complete cycle of the upper 3 db frequency limit.

Time Measurements

Ordinarily the graph lines on the oscilloscope graticule (Fig. 5-4A) are used for instantaneous voltage measurements plotted against time. Elapsed time is indicated by horizontal distance, from left to right, across the cathode-ray tube screen.

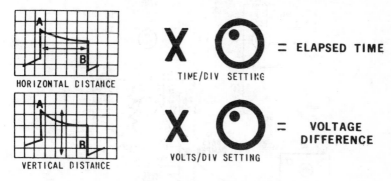

Fig. 5-4. Diagram showing elapsed time and voltage difference measurements.

The instantaneous voltage of the waveform we see is measured vertically on the screen. To find the elapsed time between two points on the graph (such as points A and B in Fig. 5-4A) multiply the horizontal distance between these points in major graticule divisions by the setting of the time/div. control. In Fig. 5-4A the distance between points A and B is 4.4 major divisions. If the time/div. control is set at 100 microseconds per division, then the elapsed time between points A and B must be 4.4 x 100 = 440 microseconds. In general, <u>elapsed time</u> = <u>horizontal distance x time/div</u>. setting. If a multiplier control is associated with the time/div. control, multiply the above result by the setting of the multiplier. If a magnifier is in operation, divide the result by the amount of magnification.

To find the voltage difference between any two points on the graph (such as points A and B in Fig. 5-4B) multiply the vertical distance between the points in major graticule divisions by the setting of the volts/div. control, which sets the vertical deflection factor or "sensitivity" of the oscilloscope. In Fig. 5 - 4B the vertical distance between points A and B is 3.6 divisions. If the volts/div. control is set at 0.5 volt per division, the voltage difference between points A and B must be 3.6 x 0.5 = 1.8 volts. In general, voltage difference = vertical distance divisions x volts/div. setting.

The oscilloscope is also used to portray changes in quantities

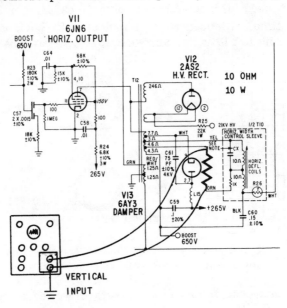

Fig. 5-5. Technique of measuring deflection current waveform in vertical or horizontal yoke windings.

other than voltages. If a current waveform is of interest, it is usually satisfactory to send the current through a small series resistor and look at the voltage wave across the resistor. Should you need to observe the current waveshape in the vertical or horizontal deflection coils in a TV receiver simply connect a 5- or 10 - ohm 10 watt resistor in series with one yoke lead. Now connect the scope vertical input probe across this resistor and notice the current waveshape. Fig. 5-5 illustrates the proper scope connection for a horizontal yoke current test. Fig. 5 - 6 shows the correct vertical current waveshape, while Fig. 5-7 depicts the proper horizontal current waveshape.

Frequency Measurements

If we measure the period (time required for one cycle) of a recurrent waveform, the frequency can be easily calculated since frequency is the reciprocal of the time period. If the period of a recurrent waveform is accurately measured and found to be 0.2 microseconds, the frequency is the reciprocal of 0.2 microseconds, or 5 MHz. At any given oscilloscope sweep speed, the number of cycles of the input waveform displayed on 10 centimeters of the screen is dependent on the input waveform frequency. If you divide the cycles per unit of length by the time required for the input waveform to sweep this unit of length, you find the frequency. For greater ac-

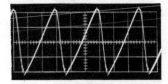

Fig. 5-6. Typical vertical deflection current waveform.

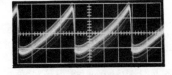

Fig. 5-7. Typical horizontal deflection current waveform.

curacy the total number of cycles are found for a sweep width of 10 cm. Since the time/cm switch represents the time for 1 cm, multiply this setting by 10 to determine the time required for 10 cm.

To obtain the frequency of a repetitive input signal, perform the following steps:

1. Adjust the time/cm control to display several cycles of the input waveform. (Be sure the variable time/cm control is in the calibrated position.)
2. Count the number of cycles of the waveform shown within 10 centimeters on the graticule.
3. Divide this number by 10 times the time/cm switch setting. This gives you the frequency of the input waveform.

For example, if you are using a sweep speed of 50 milliseconds per centimeter, and if you count 7.2 cycles in 10 centimeters, the frequency is 7.2 cycles divided by 50 milliseconds times 10, or 500 milliseconds. 500 milliseconds = 500 x .001 seconds or .5 seconds. 7/2 cycles per 1/2 second gives you 14.4 cycles per second.

Voltage Measurements

The specific examples that follow are intended to show the general voltage measurement procedure, and they can be modified to suit different applications.

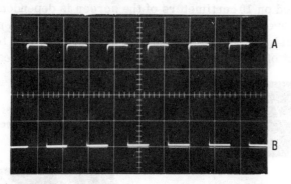

Fig. 5-8. With a 10x multiplier probe this waveform measures 4v p-p.

MEASUREMENT OF PEAK-TO-PEAK VOLTAGES: Suppose a given waveform produces the trace shown in Fig. 5-8 when a 10x probe is used and when the controls are set up as follows:

AC - DC input selector .... AC
Volts/cm Control 1
Variable Control .... Calibrated

The first step in determining the p-p voltage of this waveform is to measure the amount of vertical deflection. The vertical distance from point A, the positive peak, to point B, the negative peak, is 4 centimeters. Multiply this figure by the volts/cm setting, .1, and the result is .4 volt, the voltage present at the scope input connector. Multiply this result by 10 (the attenuation ratio of the probe). This gives 4 volts as the p-p voltage for the displayed waveform.

MEASUREMENT OF P-P WAVEFORM VOLTAGE WITH RE-
SPECT TO GROUND: Set the AC-DC input selector switch to
DC, the variable control to calibrated, and adjust the oscilloscope for a free-running trace. Touch the probe tip to the
oscilloscope ground terminal (use the vertical position control to set the trace at a convenient position, such as B, in
Fig. 5-9). Next, disconnect the probe tip from the ground
terminal and connect it to the signal source, without touching
the vertical position control. Adjust the oscilloscope controls
for a stable display.

Observe the vertical distance between the peak waveform
voltage (A), and the original trace position (B). If this dis-

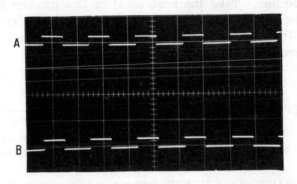

Fig. 5-9. Method of measuring p-p waveform
with respect to ground (see text).

tance is inconveniently large or small, reset the volts/cm
switch to a more suitable position and repeat the above procedure. For example, suppose the vertical distance between
A and B is 4 centimeters when a 10x probe is used and when
the volts/cm switch is set at 0.1. Multiply the distance between A and B (4 cm) by the volts/cm setting (0.1v/cm) and by
the probe attenuation ratio (10). This shows the peak voltage
of the waveform with respect to ground as 4 volts.

While measuring signal amplitudes, it is important to remember that the width of the trace may be an appreciable part
of the overall measurement. This is particularly true when
you are measuring signals of small amplitude or when stray-
signal pick up has broadened the trace. Notice in Fig. 5-8 that
points A and B correspond to the bottom side of the trace itself.
The measurement would be just as accurate, whether points
A and B correspond to the top side of the trace or to its center.

Pulse Repetition Rate

The quantity called pulse repetition rate (or pulse frequency) for periodic pulses can be expressed as the number of pulses per unit of time—10 pulses (or cycles) per second; 50 pulses (or cycles), per microsecond, for instance. When using the oscilloscope to measure the frequency or repetition rate of a periodic waveform, first read the horizontal distance in major graticule divisions between corresponding points on two succeeding waves. This distance is the horizontal distance occupied by one cycle of the wave. Multiply this distance by the setting of the time/div. control in seconds, milliseconds, or microseconds. Take the reciprocal of this product (that is divide the product into 1). The result is the desired frequency or repetition rate in cycles per second, per millisecond, or per microsecond:

$$\text{REPETITION RATE (or frequency)} = \frac{1}{\text{horizontal distance occupied by one cycle} \times \text{time/div. setting.}}$$

DUTY FACTOR OF PULSES: For periodic pulses, the duty factor, or duty cycle, is equal to the duration of a pulse multiplied by the pulse repetition rate (or divided by the period of the pulse). The pulse duration is the interval of time between the first and last instants at which the pulse voltage reaches some specified percentage of the peak voltage of the pulse. The duty factor is often expressed as a percentage. (Notice that the duty factor defined here is the ratio of "on" time to the total time for one cycle. This is different from another common use of "duty factor"—the ratio of average power to peak power. The two usages give equal values only in the case of rectangular pulses and certain other special pulses.)

PULSE ON-OFF TIME RATIO: This is the ratio of the "on" time of a pulse to the "off" time (between pulses). For example, the on and off time of the horizontal sweep oscillator in a transistor TV receiver must be measured and adjusted correctly.

Writing Rate

An oscilloscope's "writing rate" is usually taken to mean the maximum spot speed (usually in centimeters per microsecond) at which a satisfactory photograph can be made. The maximum writing rate that can be observed depends not only on the response of the horizontal and vertical deflection systems of the scope and the characteristics of the CRT, but also upon the photographic equipment and processes used.

Square-Wave Interpretation

It can be shown that a periodic nonsinusoidal wave is equivalent to the sum of:

1. A fundamental wave—that is, a sine wave whose frequency is equal to the frequency of the original nonsinusoidal wave.
2. And a series of harmonics—sine waves whose frequencies are whole numbers multiplied by the fundamental frequency.

The various sine waves just mentioned are called components of the original nonsinusoidal wave. With appropriate equipment, we could either (a) break down the original nonsinusoidal wave into its fundamental and harmonic sine-wave components, or (b) combine an appropriate set of sine waves to produce a desired nonsinusoidal waveform. We shall not concern ourselves here with actually performing either of these operations. But the fact that a sequence of periodic pulses is equivalent to an appropriate set of sine-wave components helps us to understand the problems of generating, amplifying, and testing with complicated waveforms.

Shown in Fig. 5-10 is a sequence of periodic pulses having a rectangular or "square" waveform. Such a pulse sequence can be shown to be made up of a fundamental sine wave plus an infinite series of "odd" harmonic sine waves. The pulse sequence is composed of the fundamental sine wave and only those harmonic sine waves whose frequencies are equal to the fundamental frequency multiplied by odd whole numbers. The amplitudes of the harmonics vary in inverse proportion to the frequencies of the harmonics. This means the third harmonic is 1/3 as strong as the fundamental; the fifth harmonic is 1/5 as strong as the fundamental, etc. The way these sine-wave components can be combined to make up the original square-wave pulse sequence is illustrated in Fig. 5-16. Notice that the first few harmonics combine with the fundamental to provide an approach to an actual square wave. Additional harmonics of higher frequencies would (a) cause the leading edge to rise more rapidly, and (b) produce a sharper corner between the leading edge and the top of the wave. It would require an "infinite" range of harmonics to produce a truly vertical leading edge and an actual sharp corner, and this situation is physically impossible to produce. However, waves can be generated that are very close to this

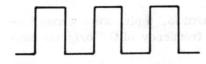

Fig. 5-10. Three cycles of a periodic rectangular wave (square wave).

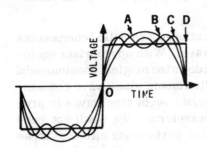

Fig. 5-11. Drawing showing the addition of successively higher-order harmonics to a fundamental sine wave to produce a close approximation of a square wave.

ideal situation. (The same considerations apply to the trailing edge of the waveform, and the following corner.)

Information regarding the amplitudes and phase relationships of the higher harmonics is, therefore, contained in the leading-edge steepness and in the sharpness of the corner. If low-frequency components (fundamental and the first few harmonics) are not present in the proper amounts and in the correct phase relationships, the part of the square-wave affected will be the flat top. Low-frequency defects will show up in the form of a slope or general curvature in the top (Fig. 5-12). This situation is summarized in Fig. 5-13.

It is convenient to use square waves, rather than other

forms of waves, for equipment tests because the nature of a defect, rather than simply its presence, is suggested by the kind of distortion that occurs to a square wave. By observing square-wave response, we can tell whether the amplification of low or high frequencies is affected. If two linear devices produce identical response curves when square waves are fed into them, they can, in general, be expected to perform similarly when other waveforms are fed into them.

5-12. Square waves indicating low-frequency defects. At (A) low frequencies are attenuated; at (B) low frequencies are accentuated.

5-13. Drawing showing low- and high-frequency information found in a square wave.

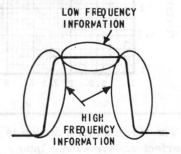

LOW FREQUENCY INFORMATION

HIGH FREQUENCY INFORMATION

Square-Wave Rise Time

We need to be able to express in numbers the steepness of the leading edge of a square wave. This brings us to the concept of the rise time of a wave, which is customarily taken as the time required for the leading edge to rise from 10% of the peak value of the wave to 90% of the peak value as the graph in Fig. 5-14 shows. Rise time has sometimes been taken as the interval required for the leading edge to rise from 5% of the peak value to 95% of the peak value. (If any other definition is intended, it should be stated along with the rise-time value.)

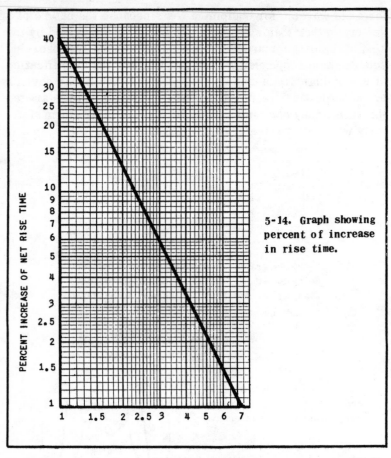

5-14. Graph showing percent of increase in rise time.

The rise time of a device is generally based on theoretically perfect square-wave input. In practice, we use an input square wave whose rise time is much less than the rise time of the device being tested. For example, if a theoretically perfect square wave were fed into an amplifier whose rise time is 3 microseconds and if the output were fed into a second amplifier whose rise time is 4 microseconds, the rise time of the output from the second amplifier would be about 5 microseconds.

Suppose we want to amplify or to display some given waveform. Also, suppose we wanted the rise time of the output or display waveform to be the same as that of the input waveform, within some given tolerance. Fig. 5-14 tells us how good our amplifier or scope must be, with respect to rise time, to get this result. For example, Fig. 5-14 shows us that should we want to observe a waveform with a rise time of 0.04 microsecond, we need an oscilloscope whose rise time is not more than 0.01 microsecond if the error in the observation is to be kept less than 3%. Accuracy of the measurement may suffer if either the oscilloscope or the device under test has appreciable overshoot, say, more than 2 or 3%.

RISE TIME MEASUREMENT METHOD: For this measurement, terminate the generator with a load resistance and shunt capacitance (including the input capacitance of the scope or probe) equal to the load resistance and shunt capacitance provided by the input circuit of the device you are going to test. Now drive the device with a pulse or square-wave generator. Observe on the oscilloscope the rise time of the output waveform of the device now under test. For this observation, terminate the device under test with a load (includ-

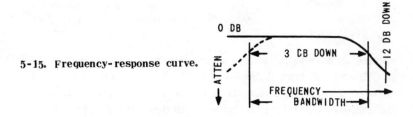

5-15. Frequency-response curve.

ing the input impedance of the oscilloscope) whose characteristics are similar to those of the load into which the device normally operates.

Rise Time and Bandwidth Relationship

The steepness of the leading edge of a square wave (its rise time, in effect) contains an indication of the presence, in proper amplitude and phase, of high-frequency components. (See Fig. 5-15 for the frequency response curve.) The relationship between the upper part of the frequency response curve at 3 db down (B in megahertz) and the rise time (Tr in microseconds) is approximately: $BTr = K$, where K is a constant that depends upon the amount of high-frequency compensation in the amplifier. For less than 3% of overshoot, K is equal to 0.35. The above equation may be written in two other forms:

$$Tr = \frac{K}{B} \quad \text{and} \quad B = \frac{k}{Tr}$$

For example, if the frequency response of an amplifier is 10 MHz at 3 db down, its approximate rise time should be $Tr = K/B = 0.035$ microsecond.

The effects on the square-wave response caused by various degrees of amplifier high-frequency compensation are indicated in Fig. 5-16. Curve A shows the frequency response of an amplifier adjusted for approximate rolloff. Curve A shows the resulting optimum square-wave response of this amplifer—the fastest rise without overshoot.

Now consider a second amplifier whose high-frequency re-

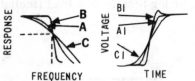

5-16. Curves showing effects of high-frequency compensation on square waves.

sponse was originally less than that of the amplifier treated in Curve A. Curve B shows the effect of the use of excessive high-frequency compensation in the design or adjustment of the amplifier to bring the upper 3 db down frequency response of this second amplifier up to that of the one seen in Curve A. Notice that the frequency response falls off more steeply than it should, and that the associated square-wave response (Curve B) has overshoot and possibly ringing. (Ringing is damped oscillation at approximately the cutoff frequency, appearing along the top of the wave.)

Curve C shows what happens to the frequency response when insufficient high-frequency compensation is used. This curve falls off more slowly than it should. The corresponding square-wave response (Curve C) indicates that an undue amount of time is required for the wave to rise through the last several percent of the leading edge. Increased high-frequency compensation would reduce the rise time of this amplifier.

CHAPTER 6

Stereo Amplifier and Multiplex FM Troubleshooting

Troubleshooting stereo amplifier and FM multiplex equipment is greatly simplified with a dual-trace oscilloscope. The basic concept is to compare the normal operative channel with the inoperative one. The following tests were performed with a wide-band dual amplifier triggered-sweep scope and a square-wave audio generator. Most of the accompanying photo wave traces were obtained with a dual-amplifier triggered lab scope.

Stereo Troubleshooting Procedure

Since some service technicians are less adept in solid-state service problems and techniques, I will use these as examples. Of course, the same tests can be performed on tube-type equipment. The basic test setup is shown pictorially Fig. 6-1, using a dual-amplifier scope and a good square-wave audio generator.

Of course, initial tests are made for such obvious defects as excessive current drain, transistor overheating, burnt resistors, and a cracked or broken circuit board. In 95 out of 100 inoperative stereo amplifiers, after the preceding tests (and correction of any faults) at least one channel is operating.

To illustrate the first test procedure let's use as an example a GE T7B solid-state stereo amplifier chassis. This is a very popular unit with which we have had some experience. The following scope patterns, as you'll see, pretty well indicate the components that caused the malfunctions.

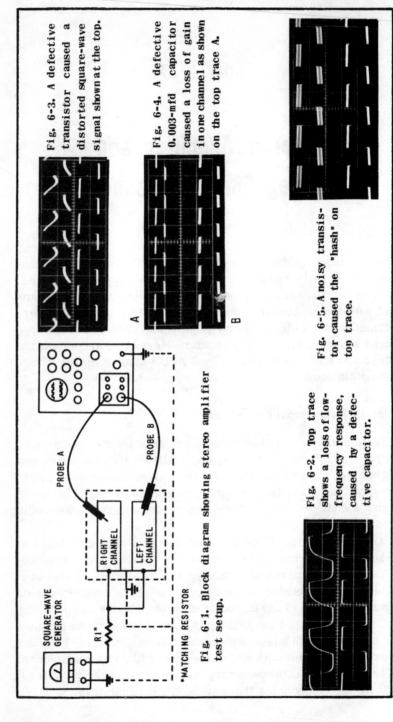

Fig. 6-3. A defective transistor caused a distorted square-wave signal shown at the top.

Fig. 6-4. A defective 0.003-mfd capacitor caused a loss of gain in one channel as shown on the top trace A.

A

B

Fig. 6-5. A noisy transistor caused the "hash" on top trace.

SQUARE-WAVE GENERATOR

R1*

*MATCHING RESISTOR

RIGHT CHANNEL

LEFT CHANNEL

PROBE A

PROBE B

Fig. 6-1. Block diagram showing stereo amplifier test setup.

Fig. 6-2. Top trace shows a loss of low-frequency response, caused by a defective capacitor.

The waveforms in Fig. 6-2, observed at the output transistor collectors, indicate a loss of low frequency response, caused by the defective 0.1-mfd capacitor in the schematic. The next problem was a peculiar distortion in the right-channel amplifier, so the test waveform was checked at the first amplifier stage in each channel. The waveforms in Fig. 6-3 were found at the emitters, while a perfect square wave was present at each base. Needless to say, the transistor in the right channel was defective; it had begun to resonate, thus the ringing effect. (The test signal frequency in each case was 500 Hz.)

Stage Gain Checks

Since the vertical amplifier gain controls on professional dual-trace scopes are calibrated in volts per centimeter (and the two vertical channels are identical) it's very easy to check from one test point to another to compare the signal gain of each stage, and for a comparison of left and right channels. With this technique you can quickly isolate the trouble to the defective stage and almost to the very component. As a final check of the amplifier, or if the original symptom was insufficient frequency response, the square-wave generator frequency can be tuned throughout the entire audio range for a response check. Good idea to check them at 1-kHz intervals, with the scope patterns taken from both speakers at the same time. You can readily see what frequency response the stereo amplifier is capable of. In another GE T7B stereo amplifier the left-channel gain in the preamp was low (Fig. 6-4A). The cause was leakage in C27, a .003-mfd capacitor.

We will now consider a different chassis with a slightly different malfunction, a Zenith 10MT25 chassis. The complaint was a noisy right channel. After a preliminary check with no results (plus not having any service data on this model because it was brand new) we quickly decided this looked like a job for the dual-amplifier scope. The square-wave generator and scope were fired up and a signal injected into both channels. Starting at the AF amplifier and moving on to the pre-driver, it was noted that on the collector of the right-channel pre-driver we had the pattern shown in Fig. 6-5 (notice the hash or grass on the square-wave pattern). Moving the probe back to the base of the transistor we had a nice clean square wave, a very noisy transistor tracked down in a very short time.

Waveshapes W1 and W2 in Fig. 6-6 show the effect of tone control adjustment. With the square-wave generator set at 3 kHz, W1 shows tone control set for bass and W2 in the treble position for brilliant response. While making these tests it would be wise to disconnect the speakers and load the amplifier with the proper resistor (makes it much easier on the ears). Since the voice coil is inductive and not purely resistive it has some effect on square-wave response.

Here is a little hint for locating intermittent trouble in a stereo amplifier. In some cases, the volume may go up and down intermittently or go out completely, or it may operate

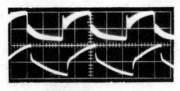

Fig. 6-6. Scope trace shows the effect of tone-control setting.

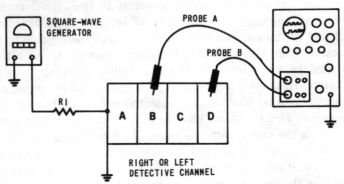

Fig. 6-7. Test setup for pin-pointing intermittent trouble.

for hours before acting up at all. The method I have found useful is again to inject a square wave into the suspected channel and connect both scope probes to different stages of the amplifier (see Fig. 6-7). When the volume fluctuates, just glance at the scope and notice any changes in the waveshapes. If there is no change in the pattern, move the probes to different stages. With this technique you can isolate the defective stage rapidly.

FM Multiplex Alignment and Test Procedures

To align or check an FM multiplex receiver the general practice is to feed in an FM stereo signal from a generator and connect a VTVM or scope to the right-channel output. Then after a few checks and adjustments, disconnect the leads from the right channel and connect them to the left channel. Not so, with the dual-trace professional oscilloscope. Just connect the time-saver setup shown in Fig. 6-8, and in a matter of minutes check out or align the stereo multiplex section. With this method you can test and align the separation between left and right channels individually and simultaneously, and it is an excellent means for monitoring individual channels. An alignment check also is a very good way to troubleshoot an FM multiplex unit.

Because of the many FM stereo tuners on the market, the following checks and alignment instructions are general in

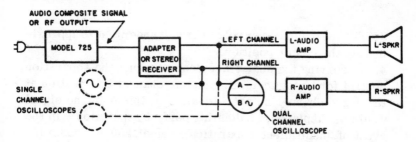

Fig. 6-8. Stereo FM tuner test setup.

scope. Refer to the manufacturer's service manual for the particular tuner in question. However, shown in Fig. 6-9 is a block diagram of a General Electric TU-100 FM stereo multiplex tuner to use as a reference.

Separation

To test and align left- and right-channel separation proceed as follows:

1. Connect the stereo generator and dual-trace scope to the stereo tuner as shown in Fig. 6-8. (Allow a 30-minute warm-up period for all equipment.)
2. Adjust the audio signal attenuator to produce an output amplitude of approximately the nominal input sensitivity of the unit under test. (Check the manufacturer's service manual.)

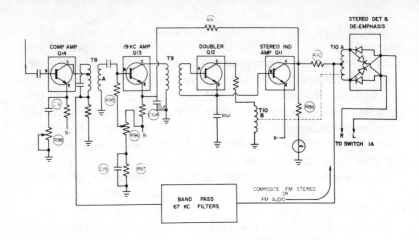

Fig. 6-9. Schematic of GE TU-100 stereo multiplex tuner.

3. Set the balance control of the unit under test to approximately the center position.

4. Observing the dual-trace scope, adjust the separation control for absolute minimum left-channel information at the right-channel output. Ideally, at this point no signal would be displayed, indicating perfect separation. In the event of insufficient separation, some 1200-Hz audio information will be present. Now, turn the right-channel selector of the stereo generator to the off position and observe the scope. The left-channel output should be an undistorted 1200-Hz sine wave as shown in Fig. 6-10. Note: The waveform obtained at either the L- or R-channel output may consist not only of a 1200-Hz audio signal but also contain 19-kHz and 38-kHz signal components, plus harmonics of these frequencies. However, in well designed stereo receiving equipment, these signals will be very low in amplitude, and if not excessive will not interfere with listening pleasure, as they are above the audible range. Of course, with tape recordings they may cause some problems.

5. As an additional separation check, set the controls for 400-Hz tone modulation. Adjust the separation control slightly to the left and then slightly to the right, while observing the left-channel scope indication. A null or minimum signal should be produced at approximately the same setting as in Step 4 above. Also see the scope patterns in

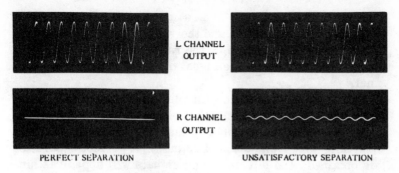

L CHANNEL
OUTPUT

R CHANNEL
OUTPUT

PERFECT SEPARATION   UNSATISFACTORY SEPARATION

Fig. 6-10. FM stereo test signals with left channel only.

Fig. 6-11. Check the scope display of the right-channel output. It should be an undistorted 400-Hz sine wave. <u>Note</u>: The ideal signal separation ratio is 30 db, or approximately 30 to 1. This ratio, however, may not be obtained with every stereo tuner. Channel separation is defined as the ratio of the signal amplitude obtained in one channel to the signal amplitude obtained in the opposite channel when only the first channel is transmitting.

6. To determine the separation ratio, set the generator function selector switch to the monaural position. Adjust the balance control on the unit under test so as to produce equal outputs (400-Hz sine wave) on each channel. (The dual-trace scope is a natural for this test as both channels are accurately calibrated for p-p volts.)

7. Set the function selector switch to the stereo position and determine the signal separation ratio from the signal amplitude obtained in the right channel versus the signal amplitude obtained in the left channel. Only the right chan-

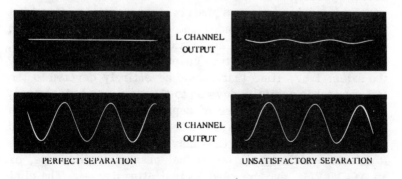

L CHANNEL
OUTPUT

R CHANNEL
OUTPUT

PERFECT SEPARATION   UNSATISFACTORY SEPARATION

Fig. 6-11. FM stereo test signals with right channel only.

121

nel is on for this test. The same test may be performed with the left channel on and the right channel off. Separation is then determined by the ratio of the signal obtained at the left channel to the signal obtained at the right channel.

8. With an oscilloscope to display the output signals from the unit under test, set both channel selector switches to their respective positions. Observe the output signals at the left- and right-channel outputs. If perfect separation is obtained, the left and right signals will appear as sine waves, like those in Fig. 6-12.

38-kHz Subcarrier Phase Check

Insufficient separation or distortion may be caused by in-

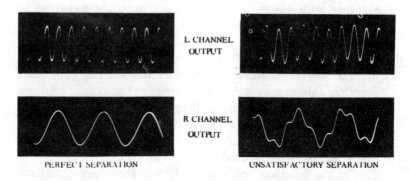

L CHANNEL
OUTPUT

R CHANNEL
OUTPUT

PERFECT SEPARATION   UNSATISFACTORY SEPARATION

Fig. 6-12. FM stereo test signals with both channels operating.

correct phasing between the re-inserted subcarrier and the received sidebands. In a matrix-type receiver, incorrect phase will result in reduced output from the L-R detector, with a consequent loss of separation and distortion, or both. In some beam-switching-type adapters the effect is basically the same; i.e., time that should be entirely devoted to the left channel is partially devoted to the right, and vice versa. The overall effect is a loss of separation. To test and align the 38-kHz subcarrier phase, either the L-R detection method or the pilot phase test method may be employed. With the L-R detection method a single- or dual-channel oscilloscope, or an AC VTVM, may be used as indicating device. The pilot phase test method requires the use of an oscilloscope.

L-R DETECTION METHOD:

1. With the equipment still set up for the separation test, set the generator signal for a subcarrier phase test; the left channel for 1200 Hz, right channel off, and normal phase at 10%. Adjust the 38-kHz subcarrier phase on the unit under test by referring to the manufacturer's service manual. Adjustment should be made to produce the maximum recovered audio signal at both the R- and the L-channel outputs. (Check each output alternately if only a VTVM or single-channel scope is available.)

2. As an additional check, set the right-channel selector switch for 400 Hz and the left-channel selector to off. Note: If the 19-kHz pilot frequency selector is set to the phase test position, the correct 38-kHz subcarrier phase will produce a null at both the R and L outputs. CAUTION: To have optimum separation after the 38-kHz subcarrier phase

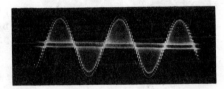

Fig. 6-13. Waveform indicating satisfactory tuner response.

has been adjusted, it is wise to readjust the separation control.

PILOT PHASE TEST METHOD:

1. Generator controls are set the same as for the L-R detection method, except the 19-kHz pilot frequency selector is set for a phase test and the L+R switch is turned on. Adjust the 38-kHz subcarrier phase on the unit under test by referring to the manufacturer's instructions. Adjust for an undistorted 1200-Hz sine wave of equal amplitude at the R- and L-channel outputs. (Check each output alternately if only one single-channel scope is used.)

2. As an additional check, set the right-channel selector to internal, 400 Hz, and the left-channel selector to off. The same results should be obtained. Important: See the CAUTION note above as it applies to both methods of alignment.

19-kHz and 38-kHz Filter and Oscillator Alignment

Because of the many FM stereo tuners on the market and the different circuits used, no precise instructions for alignment of the 19-kHz and 38-kHz filters or oscillators are practical. Therefore, the following instructions are of a general nature and must be used with each manufacturer's instructions.

All stereo equipment must employ some means to regenerate the subcarrier. In some circuits the subcarrier is derived directly from the 19-kHz pilot signal by filtering the 19-kHz signal and then doubling it to obtain the 38-kHz subcarrier signal for re-insertion. Other circuits use 19-kHz or 38-kHz oscillators which are synchronized by the 19-kHz pilot frequency. Therefore, to align this part of a stereo circuit, strict adherence to the procedure outlined by the manufacturer is recommended. The signal generator CW output should be

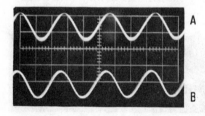

A

B

Fig. 6-14. Sine waves produced by a mistracking stylus (A); proper tracking stylus (B).

accurate to within ± 2 Hz for alignment of the 19-kHz filter (resonating) circuits and locked oscillators, with an amplitude around 0.4 volts p-p with the audio signal attenuator turned fully clockwise. (The 19-kHz signal amplitude should be 10% of the input sensitivity of the stereo unit as specified by the set maker.) If an FM stereo tuner is to be tested, no adjustment of the 19-kHz level is necessary, as the above condition has been met in the RF output.

38-kHz and a 67-kHz CW signals also are needed for alignment of the various filters. In general, the 67-kHz rejection filter or trap is adjusted for maximum rejection. Set the generator function switch to 67 kHz. Connect an oscilloscope to the output of the 67-kHz trap and adjust for a minimum signal output. Bandpass filters with a range of from 23-53 kHz combine the function of eliminating the SCA subcarrier and of passing the L-R sidebands. Alignment procedures generally include peaking the filter at 38 kHz with maximum rejection at 67 kHz.

Tuner Response Check

If the FM tuner is not ideal in terms of flatness or response, and if it lacks phase shift, the stereo composite signal will not be faithfully reproduced. It is also desirable to know the recovered signal amplitude at the multiplex output jack at peak deviation (75 kHz = 100% FM modulation). Ideally, it should match the stated input sensitivity. To check both the response and the obtained output signal, connect the generator to the tuner and set the RF tuning control to approximately 98 MHz. Set the scope vertical input selector to approximately 4v p-p. Very carefully adjust the tuner dial to the point (about 98 MHz) where a pattern as shown in Fig. 6-13 is obtained, adjust the tuning dial slightly to the right and to the left to make certain it is tuned to the right frequency.

When properly tuned the signal will have the appearance of the waveform in Fig. 6-13. If it shows a concave bowing in the baseline, the higher frequencies (L-R sidebands) are attenuated. (A small amount is normal for most tuners.) Excessive baseline tilt indicates poor low-frequency response. But if the baseline is distorted, other than an even bowing, phase response is poor. If the effects mentioned above are considerable, a realignment is recommended. With the 19-kHz pilot frequency control set to normal phase (10% position), measure the signal amplitude displayed on the scope. For good stereo performance the signal amplitude should not deviate greatly from the specified input sensitivity of the multiplex unit in which it is used.

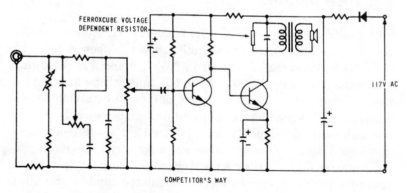

Fig. 6-15. Schematic of a transformer-coupled solid-state amplifier output stage.

Using a Stereo Test Record for Fast Checks

Stylus tracking, cartridge output, and channel separation can be checked quickly and accurately with a dual-channel scope. For the stylus tracking test, start with the lowest-velocity band on the test record. If proper tracking is observed, move on to a higher-velocity band. Once mistracking is observed, try and correct it at this time. The effect caused by a mistracking stylus is shown in Fig. 6-14A. The sine wave illustrated in Fig. 6-14B indicates proper tracking.

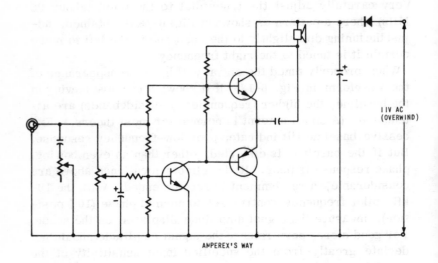

Fig. 6-16. A typical complementary symmetry audio amplifier schematic.

To check cartridge output, first balance the stereo amplifier for the same gain from each channel. Then select the 1000-Hz band on the test record with right and left recording and notice the scope patterns for the equal shape and amplitude. If they are not the same, the cartridge or stylus is defective. To check channel separation, disconnect the right-channel lead to the amplifier and play the 1000-Hz left-channel-modulated band. Now watch the scope for any 1000-Hz signal coming from the amplifier's right channel. If none, use the test record's 1000-Hz right-channel-modulated band to check for separation of the left-channel amplifier. (RCA recently issued test record No. 12-5-105 with facilities for these checks.)

"Complementary Symmetry" Stereo Amplifiers

Complementary symmetry is not a new audio engineering approach, but it has long been an audio designer's dream—a textbook approach! What is new in the past few years is matched, paired transistors, dual heat sinks, simplified circuits, and application reports. Figs. 6-15 and 16 show a typical complementary symmetry audio amplifier. As you'll notice, in both the complementary symmetry designs all transformers (except the output transformer in Fig. 6-15) are eliminated to achieve better performance, with lower cost and smaller size. Since a PNP and an NPN transistor are used as the output pair, the electron current flow is opposite

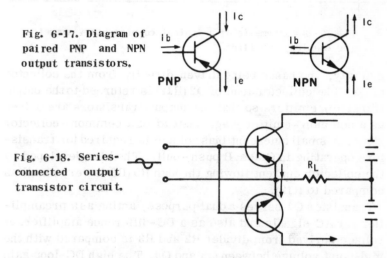

Fig. 6-17. Diagram of paired PNP and NPN output transistors.

Fig. 6-18. Series-connected output transistor circuit.

one another as indicated in Fig. 6-17. The two transistors are connected in series (as shown in Fig. 6-18) to permit a single-ended stage to drive them as a Class B single-ended push-pull output, each transistor conducting during one half of each cycle.

A typical complementary symmetry (DC-coupled) amplifier circuit is shown in Fig. 6-19. It consists of a complementary push-pull output stage, a PNP driver stage, and an NPN pre-amplifier stage. The features of the design are the economy effected in the number of components required and the extremely good stability of the DC potential between Q3 and Q4, giving little variation of output with temperature changes.

The load is capacitively coupled to the emitters in the nor-

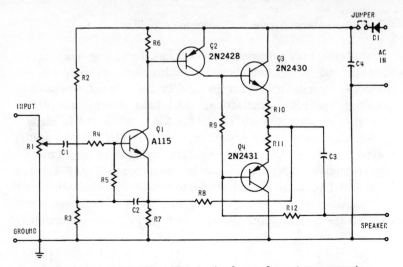

Fig. 6-19. Schematic of a typical complementary symmetry (DC coupled) amplifier.

mal way, the bases being driven directly from the collector of Q2. The collector load of Q2 (R12) is returned to the output transistor emitters so that the output transistors are driven as a common-emitter stage instead of a common-collector stage. A small quiescent bias voltage is required for transistors operating in Class B push-pull. The bias developed by the collector current flowing through R9 (R9 is very small as compared to R12).

Transistor Q1 serves a dual purpose, acting as a preamplifier for AC signals and also as a DC-difference amplifier. A voltage derived from divider R2 and R3 is compared with the mid-point voltage between Q3 and Q4. The high DC-loop gain of the circuit keeps the mid-point voltage constant between Q3 and Q4, irrespective of spreads in the characteristics of Q1 and Q2 and the tolerance variations in the values of R4, R5, R6, and R12. Negative feedback is applied (via R8 from the output stage) to the emitter of Q1. Bootstrapping is provided by capacitor C2 to maintain the high input impedance of Q1, while providing a low-resistance bias source at its base.

Transistor Thermal Stability

Workable equations for Class B thermal stability just don't exist; either they are too complex to be usable or they don't really accommodate all the possible variables. In fact, thermal "run away" is a big problem for all transistor circuits. Now it seems a transistor device that works well at high frequencies, and one that isn't bothered by temperature problems, has been developed by Dr. Shockley, the co-inventor of the original transistor in 1948 at Bell labs. The new device uses the "avalanche" effect, which causes a semiconductor to change suddenly into a good conductor when a certain voltage is applied. At that point, the applied voltage stays the same no matter how much current flows, so avalanche diodes are widely used as voltage regulators. By adding another section to the diode, you can control the amount of current flowing through the device under avalanche conditions. This means that it could be used as an amplifier like an ordinary transistor.

The advantage of this new device is that in high-power operation, where much heat is generated, it won't develop hot spots as ordinary transistors do. This is because higher temperatures increase the voltage at which avalanche occurs, so that if it gets too hot the avalanche transistor automatically shuts down before it damages itself.

CHAPTER 7

Making Solid-State
TV Servicing Easier

A quick peek in the old crystal ball reveals that in the next few years most TV receivers will contain IC units or modules and a number of transistors. Just how do you go about troubleshooting these cantankerous electronic wonders? Follow along now, while we conjure up some techniques for isolating defects and reveal some actual component failures and circuit malfunctions.

Solid-State TV Servicing Tips

When troubleshooting solid-state circuits, key measurements generally will localize the trouble. So before probing around, taking measurements, and replacing components, the technician should be alerted to some service "don'ts."

- Don't probe around and into energized circuitry—a short from base to collector will most always destroy a transistor. (In direct-coupled stages many transistors may go Kaput as well.) Always turn off the power to the set before connecting or disconnecting test leads.
- Don't change components with the power applied—the only time power should be on is when taking measurements. Be careful! Transistors can be destroyed almost instantly (as compared with tubes which can often take moderate overloads in stride for a long time.)
- Don't use test instruments that are not well isolated from the AC line when making measurements on equipment connected to the same power source (even if equipment is turned off). This prevents cross-grounds. Check all test instruments and use an isolation transformer on the chassis under test if necessary.
- Don't solder or unsolder transistor leads without using a

heat - sink clip. This prevents damage to heat - sensitive solid-state components. Long-nose pliers make good heat sinks.

- Don't arc the high voltage for a HV test. Transient voltage spikes can ruin transistors fast.
- Don't short capacitors across circuits for a test. This also may cause transistor failure should a high-value capacitor be involved.
- Don't operate the set with the yoke disconnected. This can cause excessive current in the horizontal output stage.
- Don't forget that many transistorized stages are direct-coupled. A malfunction in one stage may cause failure in another stage.

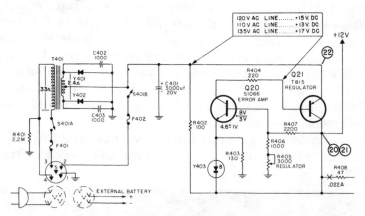

Fig. 7-1. Schematic of GE's transistorized TA chassis power supply.

- Don't use just any ohmmeter for resistance checks. The voltage at the test leads may exceed the current or voltage limits of the transistor under test. (The lower resistance scales on 20,000 ohms/volt meters are usually safe for short or open tests.)
- Don't forget to reverse leads when making resistance checks. The reading should be the same either way. A different reading usually means a transistor junction is affecting the readings.

Checking a GE TA Chassis

A little GE TA chassis came to the bench for some attention; the service tag notation said: dead set—no raster and no audio. Well, like the saying goes, you have got to start some place! This set has a regulated 12-volt B+ power supply (Fig. 7-1), so let's check for the 12 volts; but first, do this: Plug the set into a variable 110-volt AC power supply. Check and replace any blown fuses or insert a milliammeter in place of the fuse. Now slowly bring up the AC line voltage while using the old standby look, feel, and smell technique. At the same time monitor the 12-volt B+ line to ground. (An ohmmeter check of a set with no defects will measure only about four (4) ohms. Thus, a resistance check is almost useless.)

Circuit loads should now be isolated from the B+ supply one at a time. This can be done easily by cutting the circuit foil (Fig. 7-2) with a pen knife, while noting B+ voltage. (Caution: Remove power from the chassis while the copper foil is being cut.) From your tube experience, if all loads have been disconnected and the B+ is still incorrect the trouble is then either in the regulator or power supply. To determine which of these two circuits are at fault, isolate the regulator at C401. Should the voltage now rise at this point to 12 volts, the trouble is in the regulator.

Now try to obtain correct voltage by adjusting R405. If you cannot, check Q20 (error amplifier) and Q21 (regulator tran-

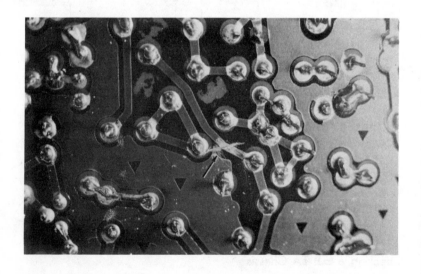

Fig. 7-2. Circuit foil slit by pen knife to isolate shorted section of set.

sistor), then make resistance checks. If they are A-OK, this leaves only zener diode Y403. A known good one should be substituted. Regulator action in these circuits can be very fast, fast enough to remove 60- or 120-Hz ripple. This regulator acts like a large filter capacitor and helps smooth out the B+ voltage.

Good Sound; Raster Dim or Absent

Proper audio usually indicates the power supply, video IF, tuner, and audio sections are in good shape. If the CRT is OK, then the HV or horizontal sweep section is at fault (Fig. 7-3). Because Q24 (horizontal output), Y254 (damper diode) and Q19 (vertical output, 7-11) have been known to short out, it would be wise to lift up and isolate them from their heat sink mounts when checking for the loss of the B+ voltage.

PRECAUTIONS TO BE TAKEN: To avoid excessive transient voltages while servicing any part of this set, a zener diode should be connected from the emitter to the collector of Q24 (horizontal output). (This technique can be used on any solid-state equipment where expensive transistors are involved.) Use a low-wattage desoldering iron and heat sink clips (see Fig. 7-4) when removing or installing transistors. The set should be turned off before the test equipment leads are hooked up. Also, make sure all test leads are at ground potential, and momentarily short each test probe to the chassis ground before making contact with the test point. Any small excessive transient voltage will quickly ruin solid-state devices. An ohmmeter can be used for testing the forward and reverse resistance of semiconductors. Make sure that not more than 1 1/2 volts is present across your ohmmeter leads, as a higher voltage can quickly damage the unit under test.

Horizontal Section

If the screen will not light up or if raster size is inadequate, check for 12 volts B+. Should this be OK, test point A (Fig. 7-3) for 90 volts. If correct, this usually means the output transistor is operating properly. Now place a neon bulb against the high-voltage lead. (The HV anode lead should be disconnected for this check.) Should it light, probably the high-

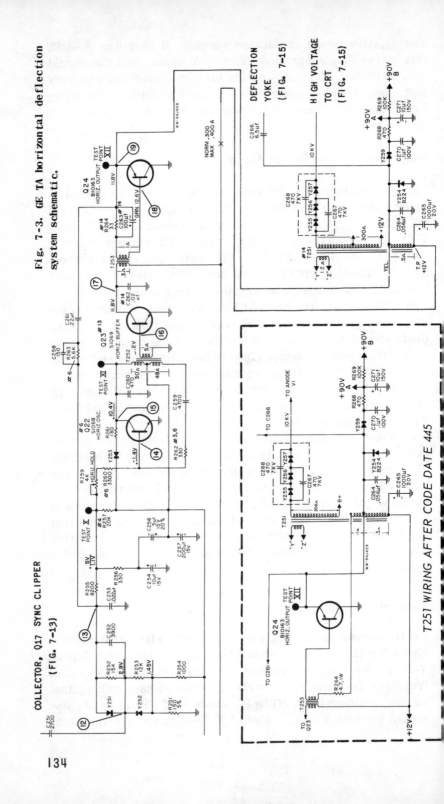

Fig. 7-3. GE TA horizontal deflection system schematic.

134

voltage rectifier or the associated CRT circuitry is at fault. A scope can be used to check for proper operation of the sweep section. If it checks out, but the 90-volt source is incorrect, various loads are then disconnected until the correct voltage appears. Also test diode Y259 (Fig. 7-3). Fig. 7-5 shows a complete set of horizontal-rate oscilloscope wavetraces appearing at strategic points in the GE TA chassis.

If Q24 proves defective, it should be determined what caused the failure. If this set is used on a 12v auto power supply, high spike pulses from the alternator may ruin this transistor. Now, check the amplitude, frequency, and waveform of the

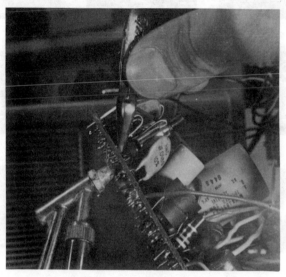

Fig. 7-4. De-soldering iron and heat sink clips used in transistor removal.

drive signal (Fig. 7-6). The emitter and base leads are disconnected and a 10-ohm resistor is connected between them. The scope, connected across this resistor, should indicate a 4 to 6v p-p drive voltage (horizontal rate) as shown in Fig. 7-7. If the drive signal is correct, check the components in the horizontal output circuits. An incorrect drive signal points to trouble in the buffer or oscillator stage. A slight decrease in horizontal sweep and striations (Fig. 7-8) indicate that damper diode Y254 has opened. Unlike tube sets this chassis will operate but the B+ current will increase by about 100 ma should Y254 open.

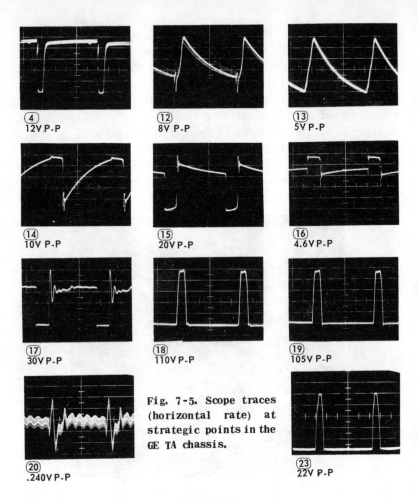

(4) 12V P-P

(12) 8V P-P

(13) 5V P-P

(14) 10V P-P

(15) 20V P-P

(16) 4.6V P-P

(17) 30V P-P

(18) 110V P-P

(19) 105V P-P

(20) .240V P-P

Fig. 7-5. Scope traces (horizontal rate) at strategic points in the GE TA chassis.

(23) 22V P-P

Raster Good; Video and Audio Missing

A systematic signal injection approach is the best and most practical way to pinpoint troubles in transistorized TV equipment. To determine if trouble is in the IF or tuner, test B+ and AGC voltages at the tuner, then inject a modulated IF signal at the IF link. Should the IF test signal pass through the video IF amplifier, the tuner is the likely suspect. The transistorized tuner RF stage may become inoperative due to too much AGC voltage. Measure voltages at each transistor, then test any suspected defective transistor; that is, if you can get to any of the components in these little miniaturized units!

Of course, you need the eyes of an eagle, the steady hands of a brain surgeon, and the patience of Job to repair these tuners. It can and has been done, but having these units rebuilt seems to be the best bet. The ability of the tuner to pass RF is determined by injecting an RF sweep signal at the RF stage input. If the RF signal does not pass through the tuner, test the oscillator circuitry. One easy way is to observe the oscillator transistor's emitter and base voltages while rotating the fine tuning control. If the voltage varies, the oscillator is working.

The next step after the VHF tuner is found to be operating properly is to check out the video IF section. Injection of a 45-MHz test signal is the preferred method of localizing trouble. In the first two stages of the GE TA IF strip (Fig. 7-9) the AGC voltage increases forward bias. Check the AGC voltage at this point. If it is not correct use a bias box to feed 3 volts positive to test point 2 on the AGC line. Now, if the test signal appears on the screen, the AGC section is at fault.

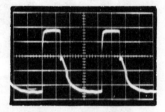

Fig. 7-6. Normal horizontal drive waveshape (26v p-p; 1/2 horizontal rate).

As with tube sets apparent picture defects can be misleading. The picture in Fig. 7-10 looks like AGC and sync problems. However, this pattern was caused by an open Q4 (first IF transistor, Fig. 7-9). Continue injecting the test signal in the IF strip until a pattern appears on the screen, right on up to the video detector. If a pattern fails to appear at this point, switch to a video signal and trace right up to the control grid of the CRT.

AGC and Sync Sections

The AGC section is composed of a keyer stage, followed by a DC amplifier that controls the gain of the first and second IF stages. A second DC amplifier controls the amount of positive delayed AGC voltage fed to the tuner, it is controlled by the second IF collector current. Bending of the vertical lines usually indicates an overload condition. Check the AGC control for proper adjustment, then test voltages in the AGC circuits. Pay close attention for proper sync and keying pulses from the flyback.

Vertical Stage

The vertical output stage on some transistor sets has a bias control that must be set up in conjunction with the height and linearity control. (Check the service manual for proper adjustment.) Unlike tube circuitry, transistorized sets require a bias control and special provisions for damping the six retrace pulses. The vertical oscillator circuit in Fig. 7-11 will operate at 30 Hz if diode Y201 fails, but the blanking bar will be in the center of the screen and also cause a soft vertical

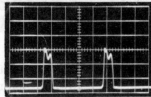

Fig. 7-7. Six volt p-p drive signal (1/4 horizontal rate).

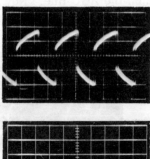

Fig. 7-8. Abnormal horizontal drive pulse (80v p-p; 1/2 horizontal rate).

hold effect. Refer to Fig. 7-12 for many correct vertical scope waveshape patterns observed in the TA chassis.

Many TV manufacturers supply a circuit template for rapid location of components and test points (see Fig. 7-13). This, and the use of roadmapping on the circuit board, certainly speeds up the testing process. When the problem in narrowed down to a specific section, the use of an in-circuit transistor tester, such as the Sencore TR135, can locate the defective transistor very quickly. It has been said that the last thing to check in these sets are the transistors. Well, from years of actual experience I contend that transistors are one of the first things to suspect.

A shorted transistor is the usual cause of trouble. All bias resistors must be checked before a new transistor is installed in the circuit. When a transistor shorts it most always burns up the emitter resistor. If a transistor seems to become defective after the set warms up (and to prove that it is a thermal problem), spray it with circuit cooler. If the problem is corrected with this technique, the transistor and associated circuit should be checked out very thoroughly. The procedure for troubleshooting the audio section of TV receivers is the same as used for the small transistor radios.

Checking Zenith 15Y6C15 Chassis

Zenith's 15Y6C15 color TV chassis contains hybrid circuitry (transistors, diodes, and tubes), low-level color demodulation, and several circuit features which are different from other chassis. This receiver contains six transistors, one zener regulator and over twelve diodes.

Eleven Voltage Checks

Cones or pins to which the CRT cathode pins connect should read on the order of 230v, with or without the cathodes connected. With the switch in the "set-up" position, this voltage is derived from the junction of the two dropping resistors (10K and 82K) from 270v B+ to chassis ground. (On the "X" and "Y" chassis, cones read on the order of +330v). (See Fig. 7 - 14.) Grid cones should read approximately 140v, or 90v bias on each gun. (Grid cones measure about 180v on the "X" and "Y" chassis, or a bias of 150v).

Y amplifier V2A (1/2 6AH9) controls picture tube cathode DC levels. If the raster either "blooms out," due to excessive Y amplifier current, or disappears, because CRT cathodes are biased off with insufficient Y amplifier current, throw the set-up switch. If a set-up line can be obtained and adjusted normally, the problem is in the Y amplifier circuitry. (Excessive Y amplifier current may be incorrect bias caused by defective blanking diodes in the transistor preamplifier stage; insufficient current may be attributed to an aged Y amplifier tube itself.)

The 6MJ8 demodulator plates control the grids' voltage level. Incorrect voltage on a G1 cone (with the CRT grid sleeve removed) is a demodulator problem. First establish a dim set-up line, then check the CRT cathode voltages; next, check

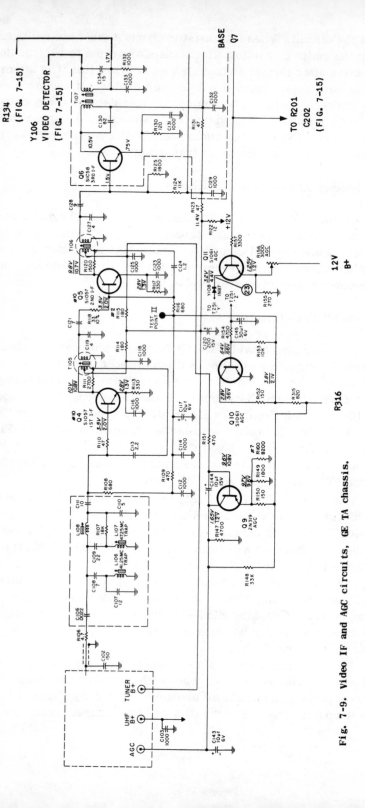

Fig. 7-9. Video IF and AGC circuits, GE TA chassis.

the G1 leads individually (floating). On present-day picture tubes (for a good gun and with the set operational) reasonable cathode/grid leakage will be on the order of 3v or less. If the grid potential reads much higher, it is possibly leakage in the CRT cap spark gap. Remove the CRT cap from the neck. If a potential is still measured, remove the CRT cap ground lead to be certain; then replace the cap itself.

Grid voltage at arm of the G2 potentiometers should swing through the voltage range of 270v at minimum to 720v at maximum, and the corresponding color should range from cut off to overbright. If color does not appear, the associated G2 spark gap may be shorted; an overbright field, not changing, may be caused by a shorted .001-mfd capacitor from 720v B+

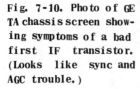

Fig. 7-10. Photo of GE TA chassis screen showing symptoms of a bad first IF transistor. (Looks like sync and AGC trouble.)

to the arm of the corresponding control. Of course the problem may be an open CRT grid, but check also to be certain variable grid voltage is present in CRT cap. ("X" and "Y" chassis range from 400 to 1200v.)

On the 15Y6C15 chassis, the arm of the focus control should range from + 720v to 0. When the voltage swing is measured, check the CRT cap to be sure the focus voltage swing is actually being obtained on the corresponding focus pin. ("X" and "Y" chassis range is 4 to 6 KV, with optimum focus centering near the 5 KV position.) High voltage on the 15LP22 CRT anode should be 21.5 KV, (output of the 2CN3A high-voltage rectifier). (On the "X" and "Y" chassis, voltage should range from 20 to 30 KV, measured with the probe on the CRT anode, as the high-voltage "range adjust" control is rotated.)

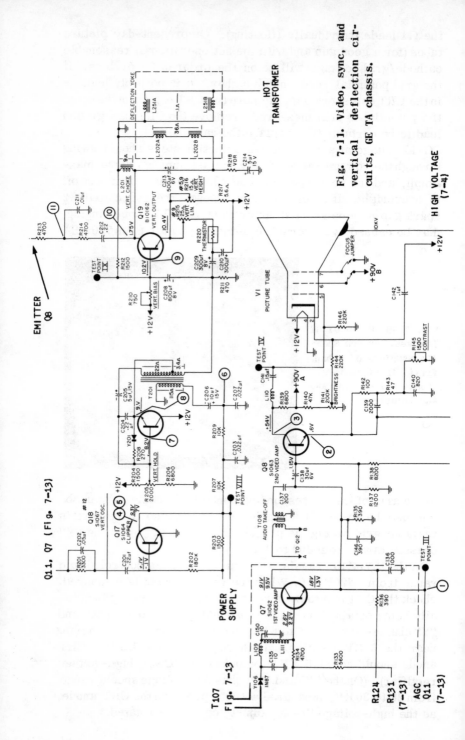

Fig. 7-11. Video, sync, and vertical deflection circuits, GE TA chassis.

No Color

Consider the case of a serviceman faced with the problem of a receiver which is not producing color. He has changed tubes, made a few basic checks; the set is brought into the shop, turned on its side, the bottom plate removed, and then... First of all examine the color block diagram in Fig. 7-15. Observe the following circuit paths:

1. "Y" information, through the Y amplifier circuitry, to drive the CRT cathodes.
2. Chroma information, to the first color amplifier, thence through the second and third color amplifiers, demodulators and B-Y, R-Y, G-Y amplifiers to drive the CRT grids.
3. From the plate of the first color amplifier, burst and color are directed toward the 6JC6 burst amplifier grid where the burst information is separated by a keying pulse from the horizontal circuitry. Burst is separated and amplified:
   a. It is mixed with 3.58-MHz signal in the ACC killer phase detector diodes (X10 and X11) to create a DC (color killer) voltage to test point Q (grid of the first color amplifier).
   b. It is also mixed with the 3.58-MHz signal in diodes X12 and X13 (AFC phase detector) to create a DC (color lock-in) voltage to test point W to keep the 3.58-MHz oscillator locked on frequency and in phase.

Now proceed with an analytical approach:

Step 1. Insert a controllable RF signal into the tuner—for example, a color bar generator—for switching between "color" and "no color" signals. Also insert a VTVM at test point Q (grid of the first color amplifier 1/2 6KT8, pin 7).

Step 2. Normally Q will read:
—Black-and-white signal, -0.6v
—Color mode, -6.0v (approximately)

Step 3. If the Q voltage reads zero in both black-and-white and color modes, check for a shorted capacitor from Q to ground, 0.1-mfd (C89), or a 1 megohm resistor.

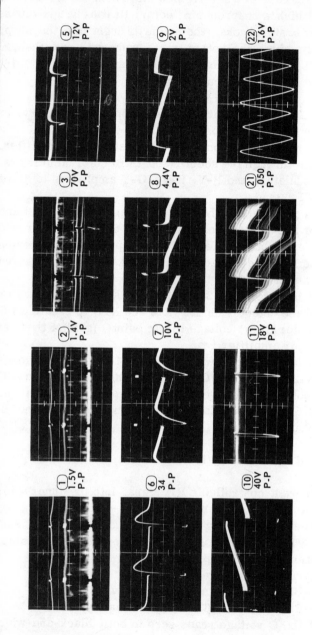

Fig. 7-12. Waveforms (vertical rate) at indicated points in Fig. 7-1.

Step 4. If Q reads -0.6v in both black-and-white and color
modes, a 3.58-MHz signal is not being compared with
burst in ACC killer diodes X10, X11. Scope the diodes
for both signals; the junction should have 3.58-MHz
signal, while the two ends, in the color mode, should
display burst. (See Fig. 7-16.)

    a. If no "3.58," scope back into the time-delay
network and the 6GH8 (3.58-MHz oscillator).

    b. If no burst, check back through the burst amp-
lifier plate coil into the 6JC6 burst amplifier
(V14), then back through the first color amplifier for chroma, through the 12-pfd and 5-pfd
capacitors to the video detector output at C1.
Also check for the keying pulse from the horizontal circuitry into the grid of 6JC6, as to
amplitude and phase. Be certain the wide-band
scope is displaying the difference in amplitude
(about 4:1) between "burst" (with color) and
"spook" (absence of color).

    c. If the scope shows reasonable amplitudes of
both 3.58-MHz signal and burst on the killer
phase detector diodes, the problem may be that
the signals are not in phase. Turn the color
killer control full on and notice if—in the color
mode—color bars are displayed, indicating
the 3.58-MHz oscillator is not synchronized.

Step 5. When Q reads 0.6v on black-and-white, and -5 to
-7v in the color mode, then burst is being compared
with the 3.58-MHz signal in the ACC killer diodes.
Thus, the 3.58-MHz oscillator is all right, as is the
burst amplifier, the ACC killer diodes, and first
color amplifier. The problem is in the chroma area:
The color circuitry is being gated into the color
mode but is not functioning as such. Check to be
sure the color killer setting is high enough. Check
the second color amplifier (TR6), third color amplifier (1/2 6KT8), demodulator sections (6BV11) and
the B-Y, R-Y, and G-Y amplifiers (6MJ8). Check
B+ and bias voltages; scope the color bar information
through the chroma stages.

Step 6. In numerous cases of "no color," Step #4 will pre-
vail: chroma circuitry is not gated into the color

mode, Q does not change, and the problem is back through the ACC killer diodes.

Servicing Circuits With Feedback Loops

An alternate procedure is to <u>force</u> the Q voltage to change, rather than measuring for a change. Using a variable DC bias supply (0 - 22v is an arbitrary range), connect the positive terminal to chassis ground and the negative terminal to test point O with the voltage reading 0. Place a VTVM on test point O to read the manual bias setting. Adjust the bias control to read -6v at Q. The receiver is now forced into the color mode.

If color does appear, the "no color" problem is in the ACC killer circuitry, or earlier (Step 4 above). See Fig. 7-16. If color does not appear, the problem is in the chroma circuitry (Step 5), also taking into account the first color amplifier as well as the 12- and 5-pfd capacitor coupling back to the video detector. Check the color killer potentiometer by measuring the voltage (with a VTVM) on the grid of the third color amplifier to determine whether or not it drops to 0v in the color mode.

The first color amplifier, burst amplifier, and ACC killer phase detector may be considered a feedback circuit; burst at the grid of the first color amplifier is separated and amplified and coupled to the ACC killer phase detector diodes via the burst amplifier plate coil. In the diodes phase is compared with the 3.58-MHz signal, with the resulting increased negative DC potential fed through test point Q back to the grid of the first color amplifier to complete the loop. Thus, if test point Q is forced into the color condition of -6.0 by means of the variable bias supply, the appearance or absence of displayed color indicates the problem area to be serviced.

Test point W (Fig. 7-17) and the 3.58-MHz oscillator are involved in a feedback condition: The 3.58-MHz signal from plate pin 6 of 6GH8A (oscillator) goes into the phase delay line, where a signal is sampled at the junction of C115 and a 330-ohm resistor to the junction of the two AFC phase detector diodes (X12 and X13). In the diodes the phase of the 3.58-MHz signal is compared with burst, developing a DC potential at the junction of the 2.2 megohm output resistors (test point W) which then proceeds to 1/2 6GH8A (V15A) reactance control triode to keep the 3.58-MHz oscillator locked in.

Fig. 7-13. Template being used to quickly locate parts and test points for rapid troubleshooting.

When the 3.58-MHz color oscillator is not locked in on the incoming color signal, check at test point W and associated circuitry with a wide-band scope using a low-capacity probe:

a. Can diodes X12 and X13 create the phase correction voltage? Is burst present at the end of each diode? Is the 3.58-MHz signal at the correct amplitude at the diodes' junction?

b. After determining that burst and 3.58-MHz signal are available, is the correction voltage available at W? Is a capacitor shorted (C169 or C170), bypassing the resulting DC directly to chassis ground?

c. Is the correction voltage being developed at W but not utilized at the grid of the reactance control section? Is the series choke open? Has the series resistor become tremendously high in value?

When the 3.58-MHz color oscillator is not locked in on the incoming color signal, and diagonal color bars appear when the color killer control is turned up to maximum, an effective servicing procedure is to use a variable bias supply:

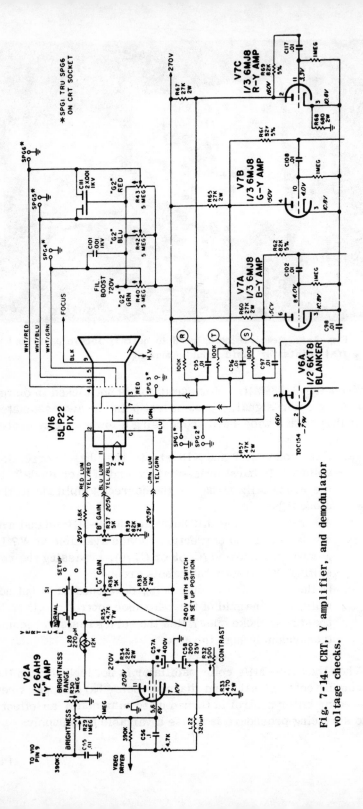

Fig. 7-14. CRT, Y amplifier, and demodulator voltage checks.

a. Connect one terminal to chassis ground; place the other terminal at test point W with a potential of around 3v or less. Adjust L47 (plate coil) in the reactance control section for color lock-in.

b. Next, adjust the bias voltage to a new value of about 1v change, pulling the color out of sync. Readjust L47 to lock color back in.

c. Trying several more voltage settings, and relocking color with L47 adjustments, proves that the oscillator will track varying values of W, and the trouble is in the AFC phase detector diodes or the incoming signals.

d. If on the other hand the 3.58 – MHz oscillator will not track the W bias changes, the problem is in the oscillator or the reactance control section.

The AGC circuit (Fig. 7-18), involving 6HS8 (V4), also employs a feedback circuit. The incoming signal passes through the tuner, the IF, to the sync - sound -AGC detector (C2), thence through the 1/2 6KT8 amplifier into the sync-AGC tube, 6HS8. The DC output of the AGC section from plate pin 3, in connection with the gating pulse from the sync circuit through 470 pfd (C148) goes into the AGC transistor (TR5) where the output, from the collector, through test point E, goes to the IF system. Also, the output of the 6HS8 sync - AGC section plate pin 3 goes through a 2.2 meg resistor to the tuner, completing the feedback circuit.

If the raster goes blank, indicating an AGC-type problem, the question is: Is it the tuner, the IF, detector points C1 or C2, the sound-sync-AGC amplifier, or the AGC area itself? Use the variable bias supply at the plate of the 6HS8, inserting a 0 voltage value; watch for CRT picture, or with a scope at C1 watch for composite information, under reasonable incoming signal level. If the composite signal can be detected, and its amplitude varies as the bias is adjusted, this indicates the tuner, IF, and picture detector are all right. The problem is in the AGC system.

With manual bias on the AGC plate, scope the 6HS8 grid pin 9 for composite information (sync positive - going) and pin 7 for a weak composite signal from cathode-follower 1/2 6KT8 (V1A) (sync negative-going), when a composite signal is observed at the detector and video may be obtained on the raster. Next remove the manual bias and place the scope probe on pin 3 of the 6HS8 to verify adequate positive-going gating information from the horizontal circuitry through the 470-pfd capacitor (C148). C148 may lapse into a diode condition, developing a steady -50v potential on the AGC plate, or it may revert to a battery action, applying -1.1v on the plate, in addition of course to opening, shorting, or leaking.

If manual bias on the AGC plate (near zero potential) and a moderate incoming RF signal will not produce a composite signal on a scope at either C1 (video) or C2 (sync-sound-AGC), proceed with tuner and IF servicing. If manual bias does produce information, scope through the AGC circuitry from C2 to determine where the signal is lost, voltages are incorrect,

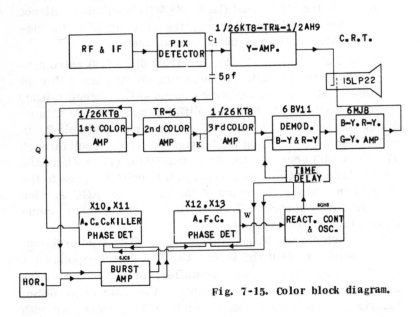

Fig. 7-15. Color block diagram.

or settings of controls (AGC, R44, R47, and AGC delay) are incorrect.

The horizontal phase comparer is involved in another feedback loop (Fig. 7-19). The horizontal oscillator itself (V10B) produces a 15,750 - Hz signal which is amplified and shaped, then sampled at the flyback transformer to produce a low-amplitude pulse for phase comparer diode X8, where it is compared with the incoming horizontal sync pulse. The resultant DC signal is applied through a 1 meg resistor to the horizontal control section (V10A), controlling horizontal oscillator frequency and phase at V10B.

If the horizontal does not lock in and track, the variable DC voltage source may be applied between the output of the diode (X8) at the junction of the 1 meg resistor going toward the horizontal control grid and chassis ground. For a particular low value of bias setting, the horizontal hold control (L35) is adjusted to obtain raster lock-in. The bias is then adjusted to a new voltage, and L35 readjusted for picture lock-in. If a sequence of voltages can, with readjustment of L35, produce raster synchronization, then the horizontal control and oscillator circuits may be assumed to be operating normally. The problem of nonsynchronous horizontal is in the diode (X8), associated components, the incoming sync, or the feedback pulse from the flyback transformer. On the other hand, if the oscillator will not lock in and track with bias changes, then the horizontal control or oscillator section may be considered to be in difficulty. Check 6U10, DC voltages, and scope waveforms.

The feedback concept applies also to the use of AFC on the RF tuners in some chassis. A signal through the tuner and IF is sampled for the AFC unit where a DC signal is developed, correcting the IF picture carrier toward 45.75 MHz. The DC signal is directed back to the tuners through the white wire to complete the loop. Using the variable bias supply (negative terminal to chassis ground), apply +3v to the white lead, disconnected from the AFC strip. Adjust the VHF tuner for best picture. Readjust the bias source to +4v:

If the picture fine tuning appears to shift (toward smear), tuner AFC is functioning all right and the problem exists in the AFC plug-in unit, incoming B+ voltage, AFC switch, or the 1/4 megohm IF sampling resistor. On the other hand, if manual bias change does not affect picture fine tuning, then the AFC plug-in unit may be considered to be all right; the problem is in the tuner itself—the varactor, series capacitor, series choke or feed-through capacitor (remembering that UHF and VHF tuners are in parallel across the AFC voltage). Disconnect the white jumper to the UHF tuner, to further isolate the problem. With the receiver off, remove the variable bias source and disconnect from the AFC unit. Check the white lead resistance to chassis for a shorted feedthrough capacitor.

The feedback circuit in the vertical deflection system (Fig. 7-20) can be easily observed. The vertical oscillator triode 1/2 6MF8 (V5A) discharges and couples a strong voltage pulse

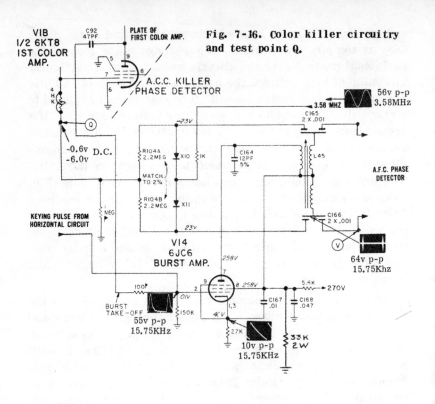

Fig. 7-16. Color killer circuitry and test point Q.

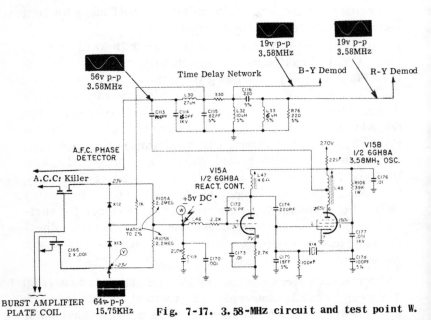

Fig. 7-17. 3.58-MHz circuit and test point W.

into the vertical output grid, 1/2 6MF8 (V5B), which is a Class A amplifier coupling a higher pulse to the output transformer and yoke for deflection. A portion of the output pulse is looped back from plate pin 4 through a 0.01-mfd capacitor (C71), a 47K resistor, .0039-mfd capacitor (C73) and a 100K resistor to oscillator grid pin 10 to trigger the next discharge pulse.

If a problem exists in the vertical circuit, for example, if the deflection is reduced, lost completely, or pulsating, the following sequence of steps may aid in servicing:

a. Open the feedback circuit at the junction of the 47K resistor and C73, insuring complete vertical collapse into a horizontal line. If complete vertical collapse does not occur, the vertical output stage is itself oscillating in the absence of the drive signal. Check the .47-mfd capacitor (C82), diode X6, the exact value of the 15K resistor from 1/2 6MF8 cathode pin 9, etc.

b. Connect one end of a 0.1-mfd @ 600v capacitor to the 6.3v AC filament terminal. Use the other end of the capacitor, through a clip lead, as a source of 60-Hz signal to check circuit performance:

—Vertical output plate (pin 4 1/2 6MF8). A one-shot negative kick will show on the screen as the 0.1-mfd capacitor charges. The horizontal line may thicken from 1 to 2 scan lines, indicating the transformer and yoke are OK.

—Vertical output grid (pin 6 1/2 6MF8). Since the stage is a Class A amplifier, the CRT should display about 3" of vertical sweep (sine wave, not sawtooth), indicating the output stage is all right.

—Vertical oscillator plate (pin 2 1/2 6MF8). Identical deflection to that observed on the vertical output grid, indicating set-up switch continuity and that the 0.1-mfd coupling capacitor (C76) is OK.

—Before placing the capacitor on the vertical oscillator grid (pin 10), connect the antenna for an air signal. Now connecting the 0.1-mfd @ 600v capacitor should create full picture scan, indicating the vertical circuit is functioning all right, excepting the feedback loop. Picture information

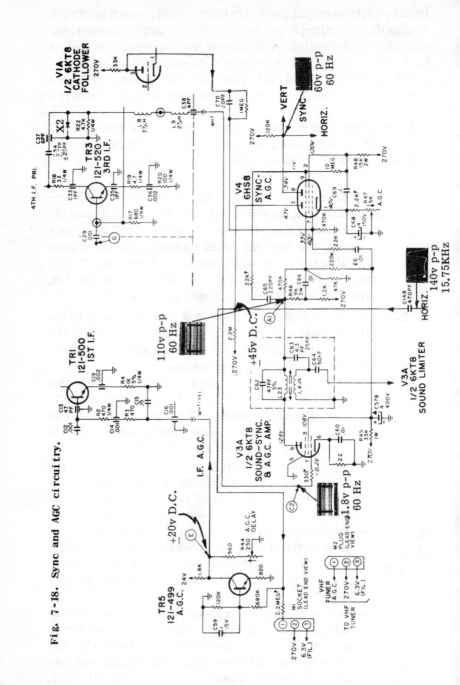

Fig. 7-18. Sync and AGC circuitry.

154

will roll through vertically since the triggering is at 60-Hz line frequency.

—Connecting the 0.1-mfd capacitor to the loose end of the 0.0039-mfd capacitor (C73) in the feedback circuit should produce a vertical picture reduced somewhat in amplitude. It is also possible to grasp the 0.0039-mfd capacitor with one hand and obtain some vertical sweep (the amplitude being dependent upon the amount of random 60-Hz information picked up by the body).

IF Amplifier

The transistorized IF section, shown in Fig. 7-21, consists of a separate chassis contained in a shielded metal case to minimize radiation effects and provide isolation between stages. The IF chassis is secured within the metal case by four screws. The metal case, which measures approximately 6" x 2 1/2" x 1 5/8", is held in place vertically by three screws. Electrical connections consist of four plug-on leads

Fig. 7-19. Horizontal AFC circuitry.

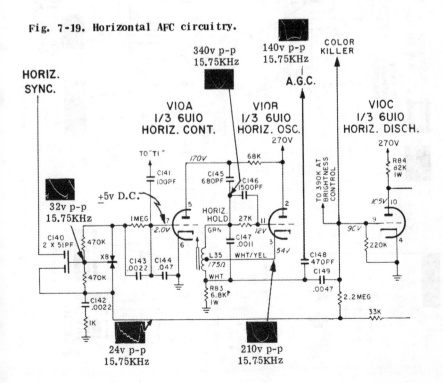

155

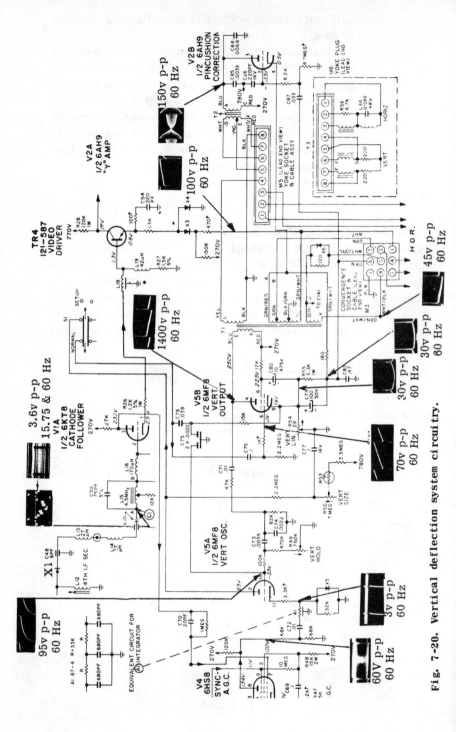

Fig. 7-20. Vertical deflection system circuitry.

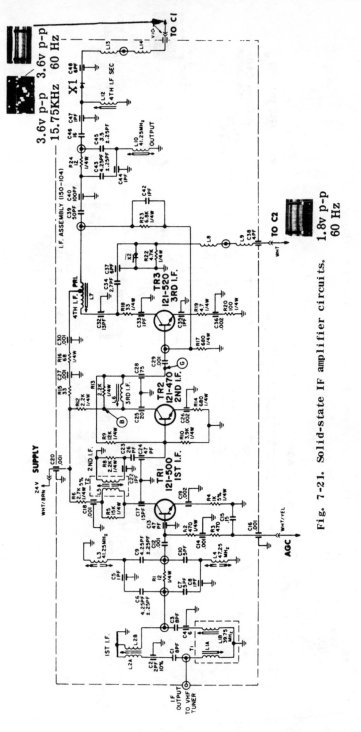

Fig. 7-21. Solid-state IF amplifier circuits.

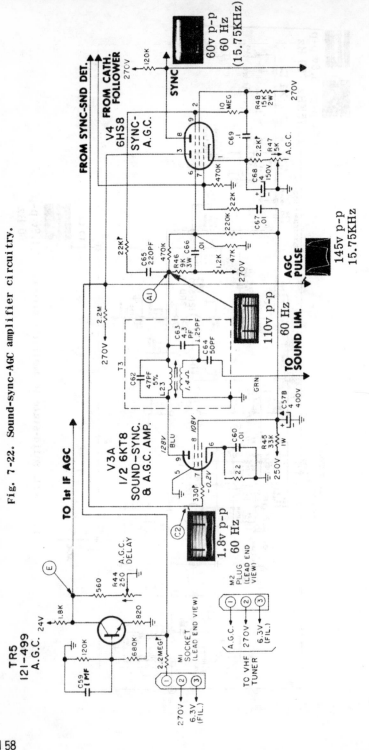

Fig. 7-22. Sound-sync-AGC amplifier circuitry.

158

(supply, two video outputs, and AGC input), plus the input IF cable.

The input circuitry consists of a double-tuned circuit, formed by the first IF transformer and the converter collector coil in the tuner, coupled through the IF cable. The first IF transformer is a step-down tapped coil providing low impedance for the input of TR1. Variations in electrical characteristics of the tuner and cable are controlled by the adjustment of the bottom winding of T1 (L1A) of the 39.75-MHz trap. L1B is in a series-tuned, double-capacity trap circuit.

A full complement of traps is provided: the 39.75-MHz adjacent video, 47.25-MHz adjacent sound, and two 41.25-MHz traps. The 41.25-MHz input trap (L3) is part of a bridge-type circuit which has a minimum effect on bandpass. Two cores are provided in the input 41.25-MHz trap, providing adjustment for proper rejection level. Similarly, the 47.25-MHz trap provides proper rejection of the adjacent-channel sound carrier.

The first IF transistor (TR1) is biased through two 470-ohm resistors (R2 and R3) in series. Two capacitors (C14 and C15) provide filtering. C12 provides DC blocking, preventing the AGC voltage applied to the base of TR1 from being grounded. Maximum-gain bias is approximately 4.5 volts and would be present at the base of TR1 under a very weak signal. Minimum-gain bias is approximately 7.0 volts and would be present at the base of TR1 under a very strong signal. This voltage level, depending on incoming signal strength, is then held constant by a "clamp" network and associated circuitry in the AGC network.

Transistor TR1 is coupled to TR2 by the double-tuned interstage transformer (L5) in the TR1 collector circuit. The unique design of this circuit also provides a boost of sound carrier at weak signals. TR2 is coupled to TR3 through a pi coupling network (L6, C25, and C28), providing the necessary Q, combined with a low-pass characteristic.

Coils L7 (4th IF primary) and L12 (4th IF secondary) form a slightly overcoupled, double-tuned circuit with a 41.25-MHz output trap in the coupling network between L7 and L12. R23 and C42 form a partial neutralizing and DC-stabilizing circuit for the base of TR3. Detectors X1 and X2 provide detection for Y amplifier amplification and for sync-sound amplification. Approximately a 4v peak appears at test point

C1 and approximately a 2v peak at test point C2. C39 and C40 provide a 2-to-1 capacity divider which lowers the impedance coupling to the 41.25-MHz trap, and C46 and C47 provide an increase in impedance for proper detection.

Fringe Lock-AGC-Sound-Sync Amplifier

With transistorized IF stages, a somewhat lesser signal amplitude is detected by the video detector (approximately 4v peak). (Tube IFs produce about 6v peak of video.) Thus, the signal coupled to the grid of V4 (Fig. 7-22) for noise gating is also coupled from the plate of the cathode-follower utilizing the given gain of that stage. Sustained noise pulses or an input signal of relatively high amplitude may cut off V3A, which could cause the IF amplifiers to be at full gain (lack of AGC action) and could cause "lockup" (a sustained overload condition) and thus, prevent AGC action. However, under such a high signal condition, the video coupled to the sound - sync amplifier (V3A) causing it to cut off will result in an increase in the screen voltage. This sudden, momentary increase in screen voltage is coupled through C67 as a positive "pulse," allowing V4 to conduct heavily (momentarily until AGC is developed to decrease the signal). Thus, "lock-up" cannot occur.

The negative (or positive) AGC voltage developed at the plate (pin 3) of V4 is applied to the tuner RF stage through a 2.2 megohm resistor and to the base of TR5 through a 680K resistor. The AGC voltage for the first IF, however, must be a positive voltage since it is an NPN type. To decrease the gain of an NPN transistor amplifier, the base voltage (positive) must be increased. Thus, the AGC voltage produced by V4 must be utilized in a manner that will control a positive AGC voltage for the first IF amplifier.

Under a given no signal condition, the AGC tube (V4) is nonconducting. Thus, the base of TR5 is approximately 5 to 6 volts positive, formed by a voltage divider consisting of a 2.2 megohm resistor (from 270v at plate of V4), a 680K resistor, and a 120K resistor to ground. The voltage at the tuner under this condition is approximately 1.0 volt positive. The 1-mfd capacitor (C59) located in the base circuit of TR5 is a nonpolarized type, since the base voltage of TR5 may be positive or negative depending upon signal strength. Transistor TR5 also is across part of another voltage divider consisting of a 1.8K, 560-ohm, and 250-ohm AGC delay control. The positive base voltage of TR1 is approximately 4.0 volts depending upon the setting of R44 (AGC delay).

Under a given weak signal condition, V4 will conduct and the voltage at TR5 base will decrease (less positive) to approximately 2 or 3 volts positive (depending on signal strength). The tuner AGC voltage will be approximately + 0.5v, or only very slightly positive. Transistor TR5 conducts less and the voltage at the base of TR1 will increase slightly, reducing its gain very slightly. Under a given strong signal condition, the tuner AGC voltage may be highly negative, the base voltage of TR5 may now be negative, causing it to be cut off, resulting in a positive voltage of approximately 7.0 volts at test point E (base of TR1, Fig. 7-22). With 7.0 volts positive at the base of TR1, its gain is substantially reduced. The range of the AGC control on TR1 is adjustable by the setting of R44.

CHAPTER 8

Solid-State Pulse-Testing Techniques

Most solid matter is crystalline, which means that its atoms arrange themselves in orderly, three-dimensional patterns called lattices. Some crystals, because of their atomic structure, exert strange forces on light or electricity and some possess great strength. It's these properties that science is finding increasingly useful.

Solid-State Components

Transistors, and to a greater degree—integrated circuits, are more reliable than vacuum tubes. There are no cathodes to wear out, no vacuum to lose, or any mechanical electrode structures to rattle. But integrated circuits can and do fail, in spite of the fact that every day more and better reliability checks are being performed on these IC chips. IC defects can be caused by electrical circuit or mechanical abuse, plus some undetermined causes. IC testing is unlike that of other components, because an IC is really not a component but a functional circuit in itself. Many times the IC manufacturer can meet only certain specifications and the design engineer must fit his circuits to the IC unit.

Manufacturing faults may become apparent after a few months of operation. For example, an internal short circuit may be caused by a slow chemical reaction or inadequate inactivation. Contamination also is a defect that may not show up for many months. The external electrical circuit can cause IC failure if some outboard component defect is responsible for excessive voltages or insufficient bias. Obviously, ICs cannot be repaired, so it is of no use to locate the internal defective component. The technician's job is to positively determine that the IC is defective, and whether or not the defect was caused by the failure of some outboard component.

Linear Integrated Circuits

Presently, circuit integration is achieved with silicon planar technology, developed for transistors, because of its ability to provide higher quality active devices than any other known method. The basic steps are shown in Figs. 8-1 through 8-4. The starting material is a uniform single crystal of N-type or P-type silicon, as shown in Fig. 8-1. Diffusion processing techniques permit the introduction of impurities to the desired depths and widths in the starting material. Vertical penetration of the impurities is controlled by the diffusion temperature and time, while lateral control of the diffusions is made possible by a combination of the masking

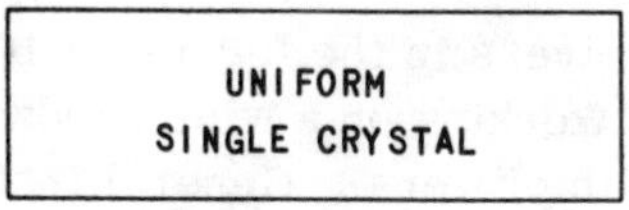

UNIFORM
SINGLE CRYSTAL

Fig. 8-1. A silicon wafer is used as the starting material for an integrated circuit.

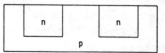

Fig. 8-2. Diffusion of n-type areas provides isolated circuit nodes.

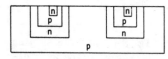

Fig. 8-3. Diffusion of additional p-type and n-type regions forms transistors.

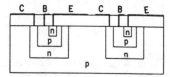

Fig. 8-4. Sketch showing the addition of metallized contacts to the transistor elements.

properties of silicon dioxide with photo-chemical techniques. When localized N-type regions are diffused into P-type starting material, as shown in Fig. 8-2, isolated circuit nodes are achieved. The diodes formed by the P-type substrate and the N-type nodes accomplish electrical isolation between the nodes.

Diffusion of additional P-type and N-type regions forms transistors, as shown in Fig. 8-3. The silicon wafer is then coated with an insulating oxide layer, and the oxide is opened selectively to permit metallization and interconnection, as shown in Fig. 8-4. When resistors are required, the N-type emitter diffusion is omitted and two ohmic contacts are made to a P-type region formed simultaneously with the base diffusion, as shown in Fig. 8-5. When capacitors are required, the oxide itself is used as a dielectric, as illustrated in Fig. 8-6. The completed silicon chip (Fig. 8-7), containing transistors, resistor, and capacitor elements, shows the combination of the three types on a single wafer.

In some transistors, P- or N-type semiconductor material is diffused into material of the opposite type to provide the required junction; for example, a P-type material might be diffused into N-type material. In an integrated circuit a number of diffusions are made in different areas of a single crystal of P- or N-type material so that a number of compoments can be formed. The IC is an extension of the transistor in that both are constructed of semiconductor materials and both make use of the special properties of these materials.

ICs are found in some FM receivers in the form of a 10.7-MHz IF strip. Motorola is now working on a wide bandwidth chip to be used for color set IF amplifiers. General Instrument Corp. has developed four metal thick oxide semicon-

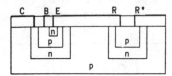

Fig. 8-5. Diagram showing contacts connected to the p-type regions to form an integrated resistor.

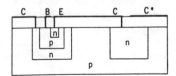

Fig. 8-6. Drawing showing the use of oxide as a dielectric to form an integrated capacitor.

ductors (MTOS) ICs for use in color TV receivers. The Type 8103 is a burst separator with three amplifier stages. One stage functions as the first chroma bandpass amplifier and drives the other two stages, a keyed chroma bandpass amplifier and a keyed burst amplifier. The 8104 is a dual demodulator, a switching type with built-in bias supplies. The 8102 is the matrix version of the three-triode cathode-coupled X and Z matrix that's used a good deal in color receivers. A color synchronizer, Type 8105, contains a two-stage amplifier operating at 3.58-MHz, a locked oscillator, and a limiter stage. Zenith is now using an IC chip demodulator in their color chassis (fully explained later in this Chapter).

It would be difficult, if not impossible, to troubleshoot ICs without unsoldering components. However, signal tracing or injection can be used without damaging the ICs. Let's first assume the IC is good, and check all outboard components first. Now for some checks on a chip found on the sound section board of a Motorola color TV. See the schematic in Fig. 8-9. First, all DC voltages should be checked, and if found correct go to the next step. If the trouble is a loss of audio, it could be caused by an open coil in T2D. It would be a fair project to remove T2D for a DC resistance check of the coils. However, a defective coil may be found by inductively coupling a sweep generator at the primary of T2D and a scope to the secondary and noticing if a resonance condition is found. Don't overlook zener diode E1D. The loss of audio can also be due to a defective external capacitor or resistor. A generator is used to signal trace, starting at test point C3D and on to leads 2, 4, and 6 of the IC chip (1DA or 1DB); the scope is connected at the output lead 9.

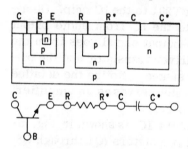

Fig. 8-7. Schematic symbols showing completed silicon chip containing transistor, resistor, and capacitor.

Pulse- and Square-Wave Testing

To troubleshoot IC and transistor circuits, the pulse or square-wave generator and fast-rise triggered scope test set-up shown in Fig. 8-8 works very well. If you use this test technique, it would be worthwhile to set up the scope and pulse generator on the bench and notice the effect that various combinations of R and C have on the pulse test signal. A televison analyst can be employed to inject pulses into sync stages using transistors or ICs for signal processing. A scope is, indeed, a must for pulse-troubleshooting circuits using transistors and IC packages.

RCA Sound IC

Now for a look at RCA's intercarrier-sound stage chip (see the block diagram in Fig. 8-10 and the schematic in Fig. 8-11.

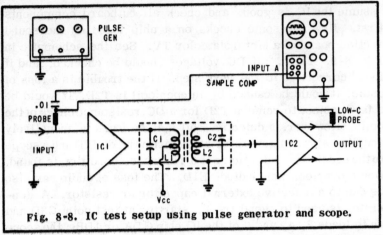

Fig. 8-8. IC test setup using pulse generator and scope.

From the second detector the 4.5-MHz intercarrier-sound signal passes through transformer T201 to the IC chip. Operating voltage (7.5v) is supplied to the IC from audio output transistor Q202, while the audio-output signal goes from the IC to the volume control. The driver transistor and the output transistor are conventional stages. Notice the detailed interconnection of the single IC, which serves as an amplifier, FM detector, and audio preamplifier.

The actual circuit of the RCA CA3014 IC is shown in Fig. 8-12. The IC is equivalent to eight transistors (Q1 through Q8) which perform IF amplification and limiting; two transistors (Q9 and Q10) and assemblies D1 and D2, act as voltage dividers. This part of the IC amplifies the 4.5-MHz IF signal to drive the discriminator transformer; the remainder of the IC functions as the FM detector and audio preamplifier. D3

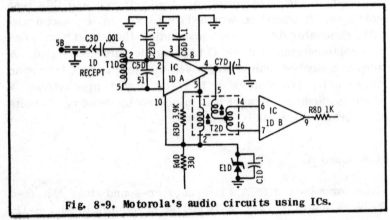

Fig. 8-9. Motorola's audio circuits using ICs.

and D4, together with D5 and D6, operate as capacitors, while R11 and R12 act as a conventional discriminator. This leaves Q11 and Q12, which function as a two-stage audio pre-amplifier.

Certain defects may occur in the chip (Fig. 8-12) which may cause a malfunction in either of the two sections or possibly both sections. Of course, the complete IC would have to be replaced, but the technician wants to know in which stage the defect has occurred. Should there be a defect in the discriminator transformer, the input transformer, or any outboard bypass capacitors, it could cause a loss of signal output.

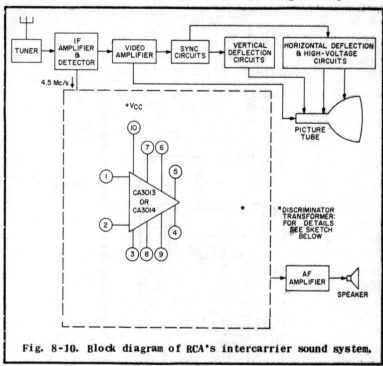

Fig. 8-10. Block diagram of RCA's intercarrier sound system.

If any component associated with the IC fails, troubleshooting can be more time consuming than with conventional tube or transistor circuits. An easier way to check the circuits shown in Fig. 8-11 is to connect a 50-ohm resistance across terminals 1 and 2, and also one across terminals 5 and 10. These four terminals are accessible at the discriminator transformer and the two 50-ohm resistors can be soldered on. Now, inject preferably a 4.5-MHz signal from a generator with a 50-ohm output impedance to terminals 1 and 2. Connect

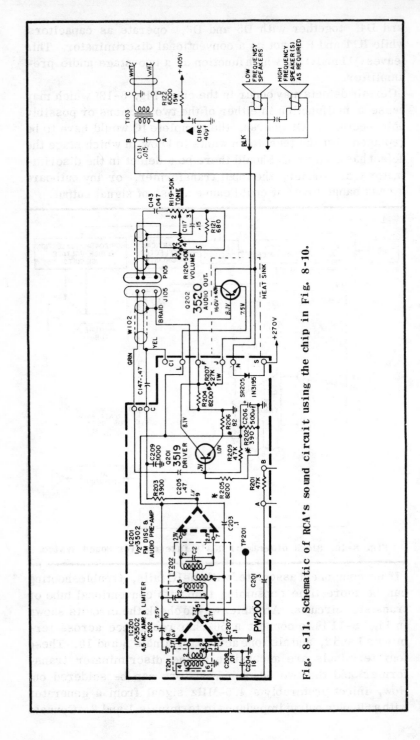

Fig. 8-11. Schematic of RCA's sound circuit using the chip in Fig. 8-10.

the scope to terminals 5 and 10. With the high-gain preamplifier across the 50-ohm resistor, the gain of the IC can be
measured.

Data for the RCA CA3014 IC used here indicates a typical power gain of 7.5 db at 4.5 MHz. Good idea to calibrate
your scope and generator with a set that is operating properly
in order to know what to expect when troubleshooting a defective chip. Connect the generator across the discriminator
transformer primary and the scope across the secondary. A
reduction is expected in amplitude, but not a total signal loss.
With the signal generator tuned to 4.5 MHz and the sweep
modulation set at $\pm$ 7.5-kHz deviation, a 4.5-MHz signal is
observed on the scope (using a detector probe). Now check
for audio at the output of the IC. If there is none, the IC is
assumed to be defective. The defect will, of course, be in
the FM detector and audio section of the IC. If external bypass capacitors are defective, they will show up during these
checks.

IC Chip Testing

At times it may be necessary to check the RF signal path
through an IC with tuned input and output transformers. Signal injection is called for because you don't want to disturb
the tuned circuits. Inductive coupling can be used to inject
the test signal and to measure the output. A test probe can
be made by winding a coil on one end of a small ferrite rod
(an old radio or video IF coil also can be used). For circuits
that use unshielded coils, slip an air-core coil over the tuned
coil under test; this causes less detuning than a ferrite-core
coil. The scope probe is connected to the output of the circuit with the same type of coil, thus achieving complete inductive coupling between the circuit under test and the test
instruments.

The sweep generator is terminated by a proper resistance
across the input coil; actually, many sweep generators have
the proper termination built into the cable leads. Shunt the
pickup coil with a 1500-ohm resistor and connect the RF
scope probe across it. (See the test setup in Fig. 8-13.) The
response curve can be checked with a sweep-marker generator much the same as when aligning conventional IF stages.
Caution: Use the minimum amount of coupling that will pro-

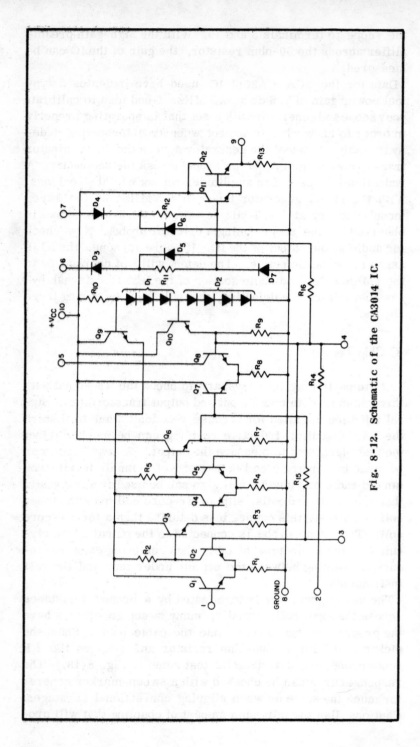

Fig. 8-12. Schematic of the CA3014 IC.

vide an output indication. It's best to use minimum generator output and lots of vertical scope gain while maintaining very loose coupling. Check the overall IF alignment only after the defect has been found and eliminated. For a resonance check of a single unshielded coil it's best to use a grid-dip (or tunnel-dipper) meter.

Zenith's Color Demodulator Chip

Fairchild developed a chip for Zenith color receivers, designated as the UA 737. This IC contains two double-balanced synchronous detectors that couple to a matrix where the desired color-difference signals are developed. Notice in Fig. 8-14 that the output of the second color amplifier is coupled to an integrated circuit providing a stable double-balanced demodulator and amplifier for the color signal. This chip is designed so that it will plug into a conventional 9-pin miniature socket and is keyed accordingly.

Two chroma signals of opposite polarity are coupled to terminals 2 and 3. (The scope pattern in Fig. 8-15 shows a 0.75v p-p color-bar chroma signal at terminal 2 of IC 2.) Color difference signals -(G-Y), -(R-Y), and -(B-Y) appear at terminals 7, 8, and 9 respectively. A dual-trace scope pattern in Fig. 8-16 shows the -(R-Y) and -(B-Y) chroma signal output from the chip. Oscillator injection reference (3.58-MHz CW) is injected at terminals 4 and 5. (A dual-trace professional scope signal pattern of this signal is shown in Fig. 8-17.) Please notice in Fig. 8-18 the 3.58-MHz CW signal has been superimposed for an exact analysis of the 90^0 signal phase shift. The scope will tell you real quick if the IC is defective or if the trouble is in other outboard circuits. Also, if the chip is faulty, incorrect voltage readings at the terminals should indicate if replacement is necessary. Although the chroma output of the second color amplifier (at the collector) is approximately 6v p-p, impedance-matching step-down coil L34 (2nd color amplifier transformer) reduces the input to terminals number two and three to approximately 0.7v p-p. A power supply of 24v is applied across terminals 1 and 6.

To minimize internal power dissipation, the resistors at terminals 7, 8, and 9 are not included on the chip. Thus, three 3.3K resistors are connected to ground from these terminals to complete the load. Amplification within the chip is

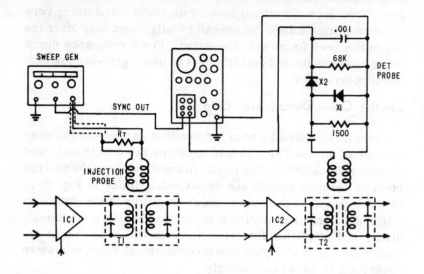

Fig. 8-13. Sweep generator and scope connections to an IC circuit.

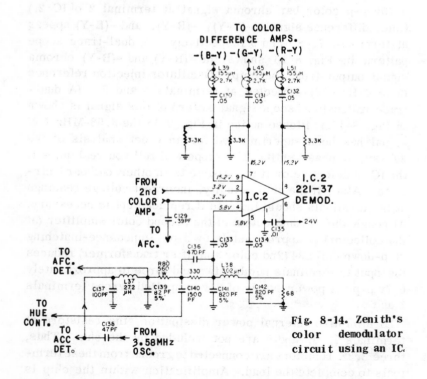

Fig. 8-14. Zenith's color demodulator circuit using an IC.

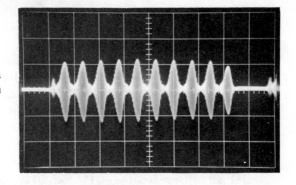

Fig. 8-15. Chroma
color-bar pattern
(0.75v p-p).

greater than 10 times, providing adequate signal amplitude.
The operation of the chip (similar to the switch-type tube operation) is such that the second harmonic (7.2 MHz) of 3.58-
MHz must be trapped in the output circuit. (The 3.58-MHz
fundamental is automatically cancelled within the chip.) This
is achieved by coils L39, L45 and L51 in the output circuit
(they provide a high impedance at 7.2 MHz). In addition, these
coils also enhance the frequency response of the color-difference signals. The transmission line which couples the
color oscillator reference signal to the chip is similar to that
used in other late-model Zenith color chassis. However, the
phase of the signals at various take-off points is slightly different and component values also differ. It should be noted
that component values are rather critical, and although failure of any one is unlikely, the exact replacement should be
made when necessary. When servicing chip circuits do not
substitute or use components that are only "close" in value.

The hue control is connected to the transmission line in a
way that it affects only the injection signals to the chip. The

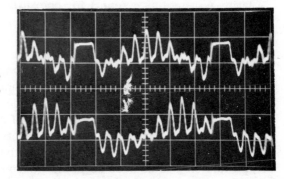

Fig. 8-16. -(R-Y),
top, and -(B-Y),
chroma signals.

AFC and ACC reference signals are unaffected. A small capacitor (.39 pfd) is connected from one of the demodulator chroma inputs to the AFC phase detector, providing a burst signal feedback from the AFC phase detector, which eliminates any tendency toward 3.58-MHz radiation.

A complete schematic of the UA736 color chip is shown in Fig. 8-19. Although a detailed description of the circuit is unnecessary for servicing, it is interesting to notice the following:

- Chroma signals of opposite phase are coupled into the parallel amplifier inputs—Q11 and Q12, and Q13 and Q14.
- Color oscillator reference signals are coupled to the two sets of "switch" transistors Q3 through Q6, and Q7 through Q10.

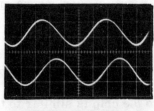

Fig. 8-17. 3.58-MHz reference signal, with 90° phase shift (bottom).

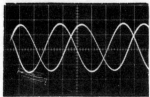

Fig. 8-18. Superimposed 3.58-MHz signals (Fig. 8-17) comparing 90° phase shift.

- Color-difference output voltages from the matrix are coupled through emitter-followers, Q19, Q20, and Q21.
- Remaining transistors provide voltage division and regulation (Q1 acts as a zener) for operational stability.

Pulse Testing Linear ICs

As a test example we will use an RCA CA3020 linear amplifier IC that is used in conventional consumer products. This IC is a monolithic silicon multipurpose wide-band power amplifier. The chip contains the equivalent of seven transistors, eleven resistors, and three diodes connected as shown in the schematic diagram in Fig. 8-20. The component arrangement allows this chip to be used as a multipurpose, multifunction

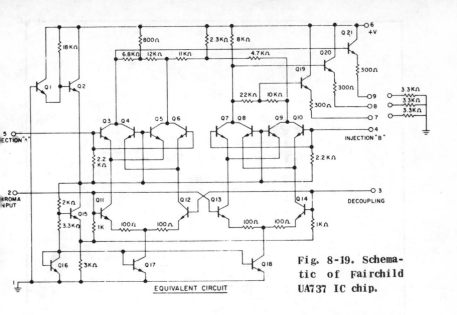

Fig. 8-19. Schematic of Fairchild UA737 IC chip.

EQUIVALENT CIRCUIT

power amplifier in portable and fixed audio communications equipment, in servo control systems, and many other applications. It is a stabilized direct-coupled amplifier capable of performing preamplifier, phase inverter, driver, and power-output functions. With a 9-volt power supply, power output is slightly more than one-half watt. The block diagram in Fig. 8-21 shows the fine functions performed internally in the chip—voltage regulator, buffer or optional amplifier, differential amplifier and phase splitter, driver, and power output amplifier.

To test for proper operation and amplification, check for proper DC supply voltage at the IC terminals, and then visually check all outboard components. If these tests are positive we are now ready to signal trace, or see if the IC will pass the proper signal. With the pulse generator set at 5 kHz connect the output to IC terminal 10 (see Fig. 8-20 for signal pick-off points). The correct 1v p-p input pulse signal is shown in Fig. 8-22A. With the other probe from the dual-trace scope connected to IC terminal 4, the correct 10v p-p output pulse amplitude is shown in Fig. 8-22B for rapid comparison. (Use low-C scope input probe.) If the IC is defective you may find a scope wavetrace like the following: In Fig. 8-23A a proper 1v p-p pulse at 10 kHz is fed to pin 10

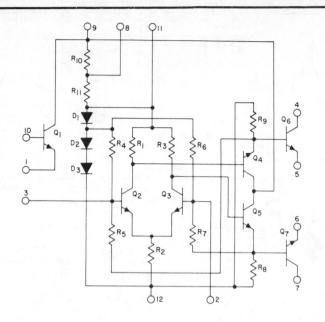

Fig. 8-20. Schematic of RCA's CA3020 IC chip.

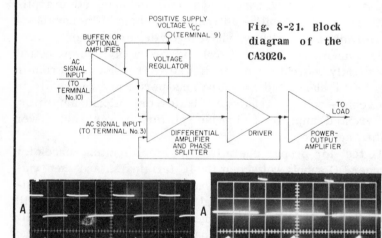

Fig. 8-21. Block diagram of the CA3020.

Fig. 8-22. Normal signal (A), 5-kHz pulse, 1v p-p. Amplified pulse (B), 10v p-p.

Fig. 8-23. 10-kHz 1v p-p input pulse (A), distorted output (B), 3v p-p.

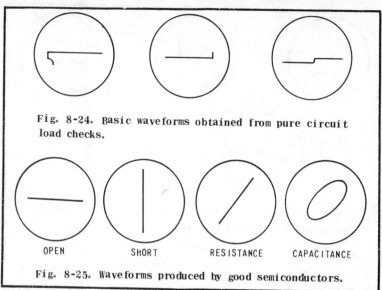

Fig. 8-24. Basic waveforms obtained from pure circuit load checks.

OPEN   SHORT   RESISTANCE   CAPACITANCE

Fig. 8-25. Waveforms produced by good semiconductors.

of the IC unit. However, at pin 4 of the IC a much distorted pulse of only 3v p-p is noticed in Fig. 8-23B. This indicates that the IC chip is defective, assuming all outboard components are good.

IC chips, field-effect transistors (FETs), or insulated gate (IGFET) and unijunction solid-state devices cannot be accurately tested or may be damaged by a transistor checker that most service shops can now afford. About the only way to check these "little rascals" is right in operating circuitry by using a signal or pulse generator to inject a test signal and then use a triggered scope to trace the pulse through each IC stage. This is a very fast and positive troubleshooting method.

Poor Man's Solid-State Curve Tracer

For a small cost, this transistor "curve tracer" can be hooked up to your scope for fast solid-state checks. This "go-no go" test will save you lots of servicing time, and I have found this method to be a very fast and accurate passive "in-" or "out-of-circuit" transistor and diode checker. This is not a new testing method, by any means; only the application for fast servicing is new.

Basically, we sweep the junction of a transistor with 6.3 volts AC so that it may be viewed conducting and not conducting during alternate plus or minus portions of the AC sine wave. This display can be observed on a regular service os-

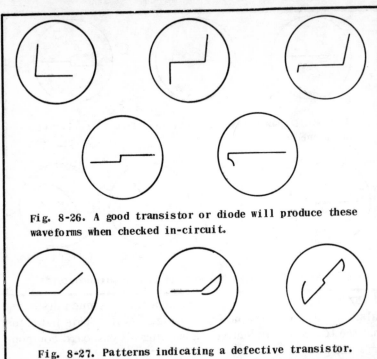

Fig. 8-26. A good transistor or diode will produce these waveforms when checked in-circuit.

Fig. 8-27. Patterns indicating a defective transistor.

cilloscope with no power fed to the transistor unit under test. Visual observation and what you observe to be wrong with the device under test is your only guide. For our purpose, speed servicing, we are not so much concerned about the intricacies of the waveforms obtained as we are in a "go" or "no go" type of check. Shown in Fig. 8-24 are some sample drawings of basic waveforms that will be obtained from pure circuit loads. In Fig. 8-25 you will observe typically good semiconductor waveshapes (notice sharp, crisp trace junctions) or twins of the waveshape.

Now moving onto actual in-circuit usage, a combination of the two above waveshapes will be seen. (See Fig. 8-26 for in-circuit wavetraces.) Capacitance and resistance may mask the true response; however, somewhere in the wave-shape of a good transistor there will be a clue to a sharp junction or a current change. This is your clue to a good or bad transistor or diode. A defective transistor can show three basically different scope patterns. These three are illustrated in Fig. 8-27. Notice the rounded corner junction caused by a transistor with some leakage.

To completely check a transistor with a two-lead checker,

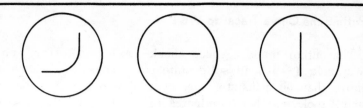

Fig. 8-28. Transistor base-to-emitter or collector checks show the typical diode pattern.

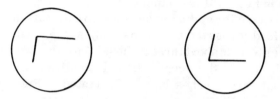

Fig. 8-29. Transistor emitter-to-collector waveforms often look like this.

three checks have to be made. Lead polarity is not important, so the checks can be made very rapidly, checking from (1) emitter to collector, (2) base to collector, and (3) base to emitter. In fact, you don't have to determine which test points are E, B, or C. Most base-to-emitter or collector tests of a good transistor indicate a typical diode pattern as shown in Fig. 8-28. Caution: Many times emitter-to-collector patterns may appear as an open condition as shown in Fig. 8-29. However, the scope pattern may indicate an open condition as shown in Fig. 8-30, but the transistor will be good. (Of course, if it shows a short the unit is defective.) If you can check many different types of good transistors, so that you will know what patterns to look for. As you gain proficiency it is very easy to pick up the very difficult service problems, caused by the installation of a wrong type transistor or the correct type installed incorrectly (a circuit test, emitter-to-collector, that indicates a base-to-emitter or -collector type pattern would expose this error). With tests on unijunction transistor (like GE Type 5E29), a good device may look like a defective transistor with some leakage; the trace pattern will have a rounded curve. So this checker would not be of value for unijunction checks. Also, FETs would be ruined by this check.

Putting the Curve Tracer to Work

The author made a speed check, with this tester, on a Motorola TS-915 all solid-state color chassis. There are more than 60 transistors and over 26 diodes in this chassis, and it took less than 20 minutes to check them all. The set would not operate and one defective transistor was located by this method. A good transistor put the set back into proper operation again.

Shown in Fig. 8-31 is a simple schematic for an in- or out-of-circuit transistor or diode checker. To calibrate this checker, with no load across the test leads, adjust the scope horizontal amplifier to scan about three inches. With the two test probes shorted, adjust the scope vertical amplifier gain to scan a line about three inches high. Illustrated in Fig. 8-32 is the complete oscilloscope and curve tracer hookup.

Let's look at some actual wavetraces of transistors checked in the circuit. In Fig. 8-33 is a trace produced by a good transistor with the probes from emitter to collector; a shorted transistor wavetrace is shown in Fig. 8-34. The wavetrace in Fig. 8-35 denotes an open emitter-to-base connection.

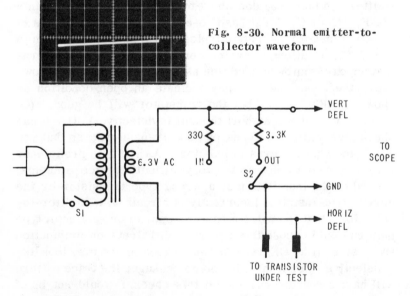

Fig. 8-30. Normal emitter-to-collector waveform.

Fig. 8-31. Schematic of a simple transistor or diode checker for in- or out-of-circuit applications.

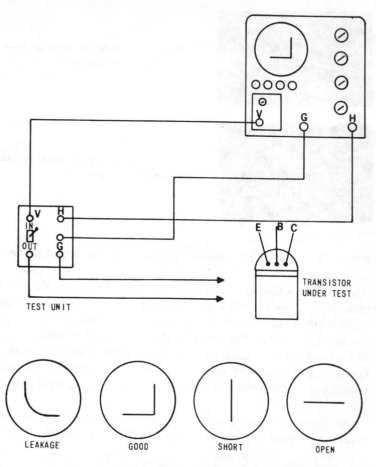

LEAKAGE GOOD SHORT OPEN

Fig. 8-32. Scope-wave tracer test setup.

Fig. 8-33. Emitter-to-collector
waveform; good transistor.

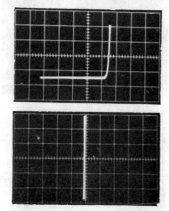

Fig. 8-34. Emitter-to-collector
waveform; shorted transistor.

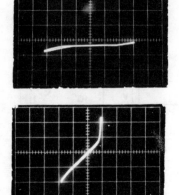

Fig. 8-35. Open emitter-to-base connection waveform.

Fig. 8-36. Waveform showing base-to-collector leakage.

Notice the slight loop, which indicates some capacitance in this circuit.

Leakage is uncovered in the wavetrace in Fig. 8-36, measured from base to collector. However, the weird looking oscilloscope wavetrace in Fig. 8-37 was produced by a good transistor. Notice the sharp bend. This semi-conductor was in a circuit that contained both inductance and capacitance, but it didn't fool this checker. An intermittently shorted transistor is illustrated in Fig. 8-38; notice the cross pattern effect.

The "curve tracer" can be used also for printed-circuit foil continuity checks to locate cracks or defective solder joints.

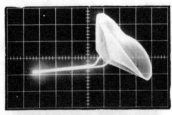

Fig. 8-37. Emitter-to-collector waveform, good transistor, with capacitance across the emitter and collector.

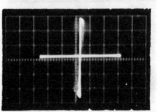

Fig. 8-38. Waveform with test leads connected from emitter to collector.

Flex the board and watch the scope pattern. Even shorted or open capacitors and coils can be located with this test method after you have had some experience with it. Is it fast? You bet it is, and about 90 to 95% accurate. A lot faster than an in-circuit transistor checker!

CHAPTER 9

Alignment and TV Remote Control

Most TV technicians seem to dread a TV video IF alignment job, or as many call it—an alignment project. With the inadequate sweep and marker generators that have been available I really cannot blame them. It is a very time consuming task to run the marker dial back and forth across the sweep bandwidth. And on top of that, the sweep may not even be linear. Then, after all this effort, you are still not overjoyed with the results.

Well, now, there is a honey of a sweep and post-marker generator that is a pleasure to use. The Zenith TV-IF and UHF-RF speed aligner is a unique, useful, and versatile instrument. It provides a highly accurate visual display for:

- TV-IF 40-MHz amplifier alignment and signal tracing
- UHF tuner alignment
- TV AFTC alignment

The post-marker generator produces accurate markers at the IF and RF frequencies specified by most television manufacturers and mixes the marker signal with the demodulated signal from the circuit being tested or aligned. The markers are sharp and well-defined and will not alter or distort the response curve. Therefore, the oscilloscope will show the actual waveshape of the circuit under alignment. As many as seven markers may be introduced simultaneously on an IF alignment curve, thus enabling you to adjust an IF circuit for proper waveshape and bandwidth in less time than would be possible if you were using a variable-marker system which must be reset and calibrated for each marker frequency.

The Heathkit generator shown in Fig. 9-1 offers additional post-injection markers—for color bandpass alignment, picture and sound carrier frequencies for Channels 4 and 10,

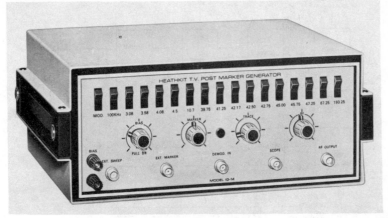

Fig. 9-1. The Heathkit post-marker generator.

FM tuner, IF, and discriminator alignment, and TV sound
IF adjustments. Also, 400-Hz modulation is provided for
trap adjustment and for checking and adjusting FM tuners.
The features of both generators combine to provide you with
some versatile, accurate, and speedy alignment instruments.

Zenith's "Speed Aligner" Generator Operation

The heart of the Zenith Speed Aligner is the sweep oscillator. A dual triode, operated in parallel to provide adequate
power output, is connected in a modified Colpitts arrangement with its tank circuit center-tuned to 43.5 MHz. The
tank includes a variable inductance whose reactance depends
on the amplitude of the current flowing through it. By providing a current of the proper phase, waveshape, and amplitude, the inductance changes at a given rate, thus producing an oscillator frequency deviation which is used to provide
the required sweep frequency output. This method is superior
to previous sweep techniques using mechanical contrivances
such as a synchronous motor, or a speaker with a specially-
designed spider driving a sweep capacitor.

To generate the marker signals a sample of the swept-
oscillator voltage is supplied to a set of crystals. The sample voltage is of sufficient amplitude to allow the crystal to
"ring," or oscillate, at its natural frequency. The resultant
oscillator voltage is then detected, amplified, and shaped to
provide the proper output marker "pip" display on the scope.
See the block diagram in Fig. 9-2.

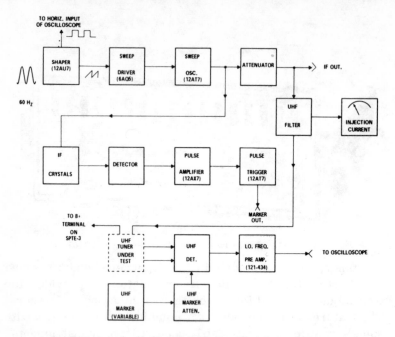

Fig. 9-2. Block diagram of the Zenith generator.

The 40-MHz sweep oscillator also provides the necessary signal for UHF tuner alignment. The principle of operation is similar to that encountered in a normal superheterodyne receiver; i.e., an oscillator signal is mixed with an RF signal to provide an IF output which can be used for alignment of UHF preselector circuits. The UHF tuner output is detected and amplified for oscilloscope display. A UHF RF marker, at the desired channel sound-carrier frequency, is injected at the detector to provide a means of tracking the oscillator rotor to a given calibration standard. A 50-0-50 microammeter shows the injection-voltage level at all times when a UHF tuner is being swept or adjusted.

One extremely important feature is an excellent 0 to 65 db attenuator manufactured by the Preh Company in Germany. A rather unusual mechanical slider and/or finger arrangement provides a constant 50-ohm impedance match in and out of the attenuator, while still reducing the internal resistance. A photo of the Model SPTE-3 Speed Aligner is shown in Fig. 9-3 with the RF probe connected to the converter of a VHF tuner at the square hole provided at the top.

Following is the general operating procedure for the Speed Aligner (allow a 20-minute warmup for all equipment):

1. Connect the oscilloscope Y axis (horiz.) to the horizontal binding posts on the sweep generator.
2. Connect the marker output to the oscilloscope: (a) Z axis for intensity markers (if available on the scope). (b) X axis, through a 47-pfd capacitor (approximately) for "birdie-type" markers.
3. Select the desired crystal frequency by pushing the appropriate switch.
4. With the marker gain turned to maximum, adjust the marker trigger control so that all desired markers appear. (Keep the trigger control only as high as necessary; excessive trigger control will overdrive the system and produce erroneous results.)
5. Connect the RF output to the circuit to be monitored (plug the converter probe into the square hole provided at top of the VHF tuner). Note: Set the tuner between channels or on Channel 13. Adjust the RF output to the desired level.
6. Reduce the marker gain for the desired marker amplitude.
7. Adjust the sweep width and centering controls for the desired pattern.

A typical setup for IF alignment is shown in Fig. 9-4. For UHF tuner alignment use the setup in Fig. 9-5.

Alignment Applications

Do you ever really have to re-align a color TV receiver? Yes, you bet you do. When new tubes (or transistors) are installed, or other components and coils are replaced in the tuner, IF stages, or color section, alignment may be called for. I have seen some new sets, just unpacked, that were in need of some alignment. Also, component aging in some older receivers is just cause for re-alignment. However, in my many years of TV electronics service the biggest alignment problem, or the cause of the need for re-alignment, comes from what I call "diddle stick drift."

Fig. 9-3. Model SPTE-3 plugged into a VHF tuner.

Precautions to Observe

Listed below are hints and precautions that should be observed when aligning a TV receiver.

• Disable the high-voltage supply (the HV rectifier plate cap can be removed), then connect the load specified by the manufacturer from B+ to ground. This will provide the proper load for the low-voltage power supply. (Do not allow the disconnected plate cap to touch the chassis!)

• Remove the horizontal oscillator tube to prevent horizontal pulses or spikes from appearing on the oscilloscope trace. (See Fig. 9-5.) Remove the vertical oscillator tube to prevent vertical pulses from appearing on the scope display.

• Use only the cables that are supplied with the generator. Be sure the RF cable is terminated in its proper impedance. Keep the leads from the terminated cable as short as possible at the point of connection to the receiver under test.

• Check to be sure there are no ground loops between instruments. This is easily determined by touching each piece of equipment while observing the trace on the oscilloscope. If the trace moves or changes shape, check all ground connections. It may be necessary to ground all cables at one common point.

• Do not dress the sweep generator output leads, nor the demodulation input cable leads, over the IF board, IF coils, or tubes; this practice can cause detuning or oscillation in the section under test.

● Use a bias box and apply voltages as specified by the set manufacturer. More accurate trap adjustments can be achieved by reducing IF bias. But be careful not to overload the IF circuits with too much RF signal from the generator.

● Set the oscilloscope vertical gain control near its most sensitive position and keep the sweep generator output as low as possible. This will prevent overloading the IF amplifiers, which may produce an improper curve and result in misalignment.

IF Alignment

In each case, it is important that you follow the manufacturer's instructions when you align any TV receiver. Allow all alignment equipment to reach normal operating temperature.

● Refer to Fig. 9-6 and connect the oscilloscope, postmarker generator, and sweep generator to the TV chassis. Make sure all leads are as short as possible. If bias voltage is called for, connect the bias leads to the proper point on the TV chassis. Connect a voltmeter across the bias box posts and adjust the bias voltage as specified by the manufacturer. Either positive or negative bias may be applied by reversing the bias leads.

● Set the oscilloscope vertical attenuator or gain control to near maximum sensitivity. Set the sweep generator frequency and sweep width as specified in the alignment instructions (usually about 1 MHz wider than the overall receiver IF bandwidth).

● Turn on the required marker switches and adjust the marker gain control for the proper amplitude. The markers should be just large enough to be seen clearly. The width of the marker will increase slightly as its amplitude is increased. Note: If the IF circuits are far out of adjustment, you may have to inject the signal into the last IF stage, then work toward the input. The sweep generator RF output will have to be increased when the signal is fed into the last IF stage because there will be very little gain in the last stage. The RF output must be decreased as the signal input is moved back toward the input of the IF strip. After the stage-by-stage ad-

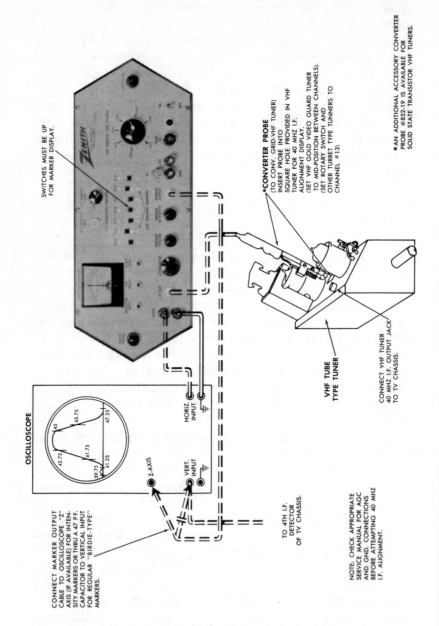

SWITCHES MUST BE UP FOR MARKER DISPLAY.

*CONVERTER PROBE
(TO CONV. GRID-VHF TUNER)
INSERT PROBE INTO
SQUARE HOLE PROVIDED IN VHF
TUNER FOR 40 MHZ I.F.
ALIGNMENT DISPLAY.
(SET VHF GOLD VIDEO GUARD TUNER
TO MID-POSITION BETWEEN CHANNELS).
(SET ROTARY SWITCH AND
OTHER TURRET TYPE TUNERS TO
CHANNEL #13).

*AN ADDITIONAL ACCESSORY CONVERTER
PROBE #852-19 IS AVAILABLE FOR
SOLID STATE TRANSISTOR VHF TUNERS.

VHF TUBE
TYPE TUNER

CONNECT VHF TUNER
40 MHZ I.F. OUTPUT JACK
TO TV CHASSIS.

OSCILLOSCOPE

HORIZ.
INPUT

Z-AXIS

VERT.
INPUT

CONNECT MARKER OUTPUT
CABLE TO OSCILLOSCOPE "Z"
AXIS (IF AVAILABLE) FOR INTEN-
SITY MARKERS OR THRU A 47 PF.
CAPACITOR TO VERTICAL INPUT
FOR REGULAR "BIRDIE-TYPE"
MARKERS.

TO 4TH I.F.
DETECTOR
OF TV CHASSIS.

NOTE. CHECK APPROPRIATE
SERVICE MANUAL FOR AGC
AND GND. CONNECTIONS
BEFORE ATTEMPTING 40 MHZ
I.F. ALIGNMENT.

Fig. 9-4. A typical alignment test setup.

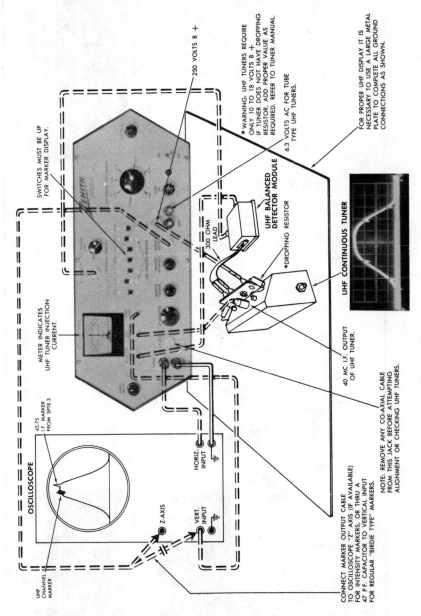

250 VOLTS B +

*WARNING: UHF TUNERS REQUIRE ONLY 10 TO 18 VOLTS B +. IF TUNER DOES NOT HAVE DROPPING RESISTOR, ADD PROPER VALUE AS REQUIRED. REFER TO TUNER MANUAL.

6.3 VOLTS AC FOR TUBE TYPE UHF TUNERS.

FOR PROPER UHF DISPLAY IT IS NECESSARY TO USE A LARGE METAL PLATE TO COMPLETE ALL GROUND CONNECTIONS AS SHOWN.

SWITCHES MUST BE UP FOR MARKER DISPLAY.

UHF BALANCED DETECTOR MODULE

300 OHM LEAD

*DROPPING RESISTOR

UHF CONTINUOUS TUNER

METER INDICATES UHF TUNER INJECTION CURRENT.

40 MC I.F. OUTPUT OF UHF TUNER.

NOTE: REMOVE ANY CO-AXIAL CABLE FROM THIS JACK BEFORE ATTEMPTING ALIGNMENT OR CHECKING UHF TUNERS.

OSCILLOSCOPE

45.75 I.F. MARKER FROM SPTE-3

HORIZ. INPUT

Z-AXIS

VERT. INPUT

UHF CHANNEL MARKER

CONNECT MARKER OUTPUT CABLE TO OSCILLOSCOPE "Z" AXIS (IF AVAILABLE) FOR INTENSITY MARKERS, OR THRU A 47 P.F. CAPACITOR TO VERTICAL INPUT FOR REGULAR "BIRDIE TYPE" MARKERS.

Fig. 9-5. Test setup for UHF tuner checks. Scope trace shows horizontal spike interference.

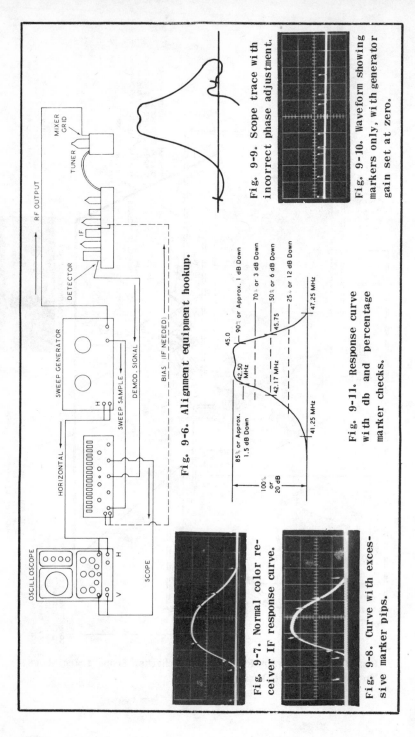

Fig. 9-6. Alignment equipment hookup.

Fig. 9-7. Normal color receiver IF response curve.

Fig. 9-8. Curve with excessive marker pips.

Fig. 9-9. Scope trace with incorrect phase adjustment.

Fig. 9-10. Waveform showing markers only, with generator gain set at zero.

Fig. 9-11. Response curve with db and percentage marker checks.

justments have been made, an overall IF check is in order. Now, follow the alignment procedure as detailed in the manufacturer's instructions.

Shown in Fig. 9-7 is a normal IF response curve with proper size markers. Fig. 9-8 shows an IF curve with excessive marker pip amplitude. The drawing in Fig. 9-9 shows an IF curve with incorrect horizontal phase adjustment. Fig. 9-10 shows markers only (sweep generator gain set at zero). Some TV set manufacturers specify marker positions as so many "db down," or as a percentage of full trace size. Fig. 9-11 shows a typical IF response curve with markers indicated both by db and by percentage (assume 100% is 20 db). To accurately align an IF system or tuner when the service manual specifies that the markers should be down "so many db," you must be able to determine where these points are located on the pattern. Not all oscilloscopes will produce linear vertical deflection. However, with the calibrated triggered oscilloscope this procedure is quite easy.

Trap Adjustments

Television trap alignment normally includes adjustment of sound traps and adjacent-channel traps. Fig. 9-12 is the Heath equipment setup for the post-marker generator, oscilloscope, and sweep generator connections to the IF strip and tuner. Adjust the sound and adjacent-channel trap to the frequencies specified by the manufacturer. When adjusting the traps, the IF circuits should operate near maximum gain. Therefore, the post-marker generator output should be kept as low as possible and still produce an adequate pattern on the oscilloscope screen.

● Set the 41.25-MHz marker switch to the on position. Adjust the sound trap for minimum amplitude of the scope pattern. If necessary, reduce the IF bias to increase the IF gain. Note: As the IF gain is increased the trap adjustment becomes more critical. Again adjust the sound trap for minimum amplitude of the scope pattern.

● Repeat the preceding three steps until the sound trap is properly aligned. (See Fig. 9-13B for the correct scope display of a properly aligned sound trap. Now switch off the 41.25-MHz marker switch.

● Turn on the 47.25-MHz marker switch, then follow the

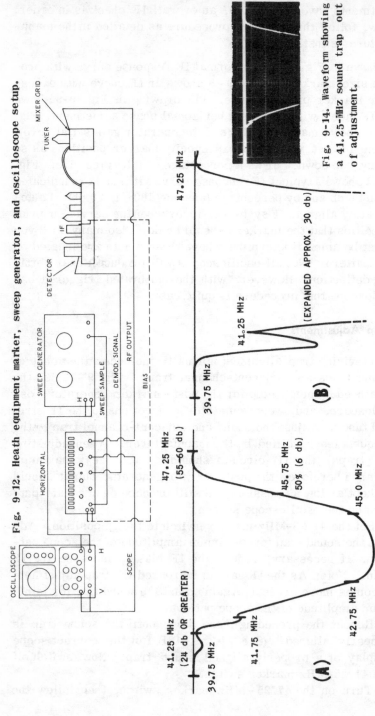

Fig. 9-12. Heath equipment marker, sweep generator, and oscilloscope setup.

Fig. 9-14. Waveform showing a 41.25-MHz sound trap out of adjustment.

Fig. 9-13. Proper scope trace for trap alignment (A). Properly-aligned sound trap (B).

194

same procedure to properly align the adjacent-channel sound trap. And if the set has one, adjust the 39.75-MHz adjacent-picture trap; align it according to the manufacturer's instructions. Fig. 9-13A is a typical response curve. The response curve in Fig. 9-14 indicates that the 41.25-MHz sound trap is out of adjustment. Notice that the 41.25-MHz marker pip does not fall into the notch.

• Recheck the overall IF alignment for proper marker placement and bandwidth. Note: If you align the IF circuits of a black-and-white TV set to the same bandwidth as the IF circuits of a color receiver, the picture may be distorted due to the greater bandwidth and the lack of sufficient trapping of the 4.5-MHz sound signals.

Color Bandpass Alignment

Using the Heathkit solid-state crystal-controlled post-marker generator, here is the general procedure for color bandpass alignment. Fig. 9-15A shows a typical response curve obtained at the output stage. Fig. 9-15B is an overall response curve, with the 3.08-MHz marker down on the slope, the 4.08-MHz marker near the top of the slope midway between the other two markers, and the 4.5-MHz marker down in the notch. If the output waveform was made flat, the 3.08- and 3.58-MHz (color carrier) would move up the slope and the lower color frequencies would be emphasized, resulting in color smear. Fig. 9-15C shows the proper relationship between the picture carrier, color carrier, and color bandpass markers as they would appear on an overall IF curve. Under normal conditions, the following steps should enable you to achieve proper alignment:

• Connect the marker generator, oscilloscope, and sweep generator to the receiver according to the manufacturer's instructions. Set the generator to sweep from 2 to 5 MHz around a center frequency of 3.58 MHz. Place the markers on the response curve by setting the 3.08-, 3.58-, and 4.08-MHz marker switches to on.

• Adjust the color bandpass coils for the response curve shown in the manufacturer's instructions. Fig. 9-16 is a

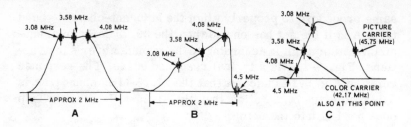

Fig. 9-15. Correct scope traces for color bandpass output stage alignment (A). Overall response, color bandpass amplifier (B). Curve showing proper relationship between picture and color carrier and proper bandpass markers (C).

typical response curve. <u>Note</u>: It may be necessary to disable the receiver's 3.58-MHz color oscillator to prevent mixing the 3.58-MHz marker signal with the 3.58-MHz oscillator signal. Or the 3.58-MHz marker switch can be set to off and the 3.58-MHz oscillator signal in the set can be used as a marker.

Checking Overall VHF Tuner and IF Alignment

The bandwidth of a TV VHF tuner may be checked with the following procedure:

● Remove the antenna connections at the tuner. Connect a coaxial clip lead to the "Demod In" connector on the post-marker generator. At the other end of the clip lead connect the inner lead through a 47K resistor to the set detector load. Ground the shield lead to the chassis as close to the detector load as possible.

● Turn the station selector to Channel 4. Set the sweep generator to 67.25 MHz, with a sweep width of 10 MHz. Set the 67.25-MHz marker switch to on (the Channel 4 picture-carrier marker). Set the 4.5-MHz marker switch to on. A sound-carrier marker will appear at 71.75 MHz, which is 4.5 MHz higher than the picture carrier.

● Adjust the VHF tuner per the manufacturer's instructions for the correct response on Channel 4 as illustrated in Fig. 9-17. Fig. 9-18 shows the correct response curve for Channel 10.

FM Receiver Alignment

• Connect the marker generator, oscilloscope, and sweep generator as shown in the manufacturer's instructions. Set the sweep generator to sweep 10.7 MHz at a sweep width of 500 kHz. Set the 10.7-MHz and 100-kHz marker switches to on. Keep the sweep generator output low enough to prevent limiting.

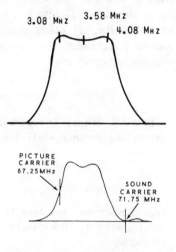

Fig. 9-16. Typical response curve for color bandpass stages.

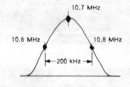

Fig. 9-19. Correct FM IF response curve.

Fig. 9-17. Correct Channel 4 response curve.

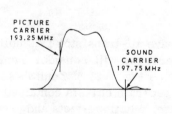

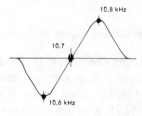

Fig. 9-20. FM discriminator response curve.

Fig. 9-18. Proper bandwidth for Channel 10.

• Adjust the IF coil for the correct response as called for in the manufacturer's instructions. Refer to Fig. 9-19 for a typical IF curve. Align the discriminator using the same markers. Here the sweep generator output should be high enough so that limiting does occur. Refer to Fig. 9-20 for a typical discriminator response curve.

FM Tuner Tracking

To check the FM tuner for proper dial tracking:

• Connect the RF output cable from the marker generator to the antenna terminals. Set the 45-MHz marker and the "mod." switch to on. Adjust the tuner dial until a tone is heard. This should occur at 90 MHz.

• Set the 45-MHz marker switch to off and the 10.7-MHz marker switch to on. Again, adjust the tuner dial until a tone is heard. This should occur at 107 MHz. If other marker frequencies are desired, they can be fed through the external marker jack to the RF output connector.

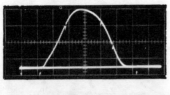

Fig. 9-21. Overall IF response curve, solid-state amplifier.

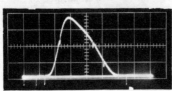

Fig. 9-22. Color receiver IF showing need of complete re-alignment.

Solid-State Color IF Systems

Many color receivers now have all-transistor IF amplifier stages. For our purposes here, we will consider Zenith's 15Y6C15 color chassis IF. (See Fig. 7-21.) Zenith's solid-state IF section consists of a separate chassis contained in a shielded metal case to minimize radiation effects and provide isolation between stages. All electrical connections are made by plug-in leads. The IF amplifier system consists of three transistorized NPN-type stages. The first stage is controlled with forward AGC voltage applied to its base; i.e., an increase in positive voltage at the base will increase the collector current and decrease the collector-to-emitter voltage, reducing the gain of the stage. The all-transistor IF system does not present any IF alignment problems. Shown in Fig. 9-21 is the proper overall response curve taken at test point

C1. (The overall response curve in Fig. 9-22 indicates the set is in need of a complete alignment job!)

"Space Command" Remote Control Systems

Zenith's "300" series "Space Command" remote control system provides three functions—off/on, volume control, and one-direction tuning for channel selection. The solid-state unit contains 6 transistors. The "400" or "600" series contains 8 transistors and offers 4 or 6 functions, respectively—off/on and volume step control, 2-direction tuning, and a sound mute control. In addition, the "600" series has a two-way control for the color hue range adjustment. An inside view of the "600" series chassis is illustrated in Fig. 9-23.

Supersonic vibrations in the 40-kHz region are emitted from a remote hand control when buttons are snapped to mechanically vibrate an appropriate rod. These inaudible sound waves are picked up by a microphone, located at the front of the TV set, which changes the supersonic sound waves into electrical energy. A motor drive assembly is mounted on the rear of the VHF tuner, as shown in Fig. 9-24. A channel selector push-bar or buttons, or the signal from the hand control, will actuate the motor drive assembly. A manual channel-selector knob is provided at the rear of the set should trouble develop with the motor drive system.

A limiter and three amplifier stages are incorporated ahead of the detector relay drivers, as shown in Fig. 9-25. The amplifier stage is tuned to the middle of the passband between the upper and lower tuning-rod frequencies. A self-contained power supply in each chassis has a power transformer with silicon rectifier X1, filter capacitors, and voltage-divider network that provides various DC voltages for the control chassis. An automatic-manual switch, located at the rear of the control chassis, disables the control circuits for manual operation in the event of remote control failure.

THEORY OF OPERATION: The remote microphone (Fig. 9-26) is a low-impedance ceramic type designed for a broad peak response at 40-kHz. It is coupled directly to the base of the first transistor. The amplifier section (Fig. 9-25) consists of three transistors and one tuned circuit. Resistors are connected between the collector and base of each

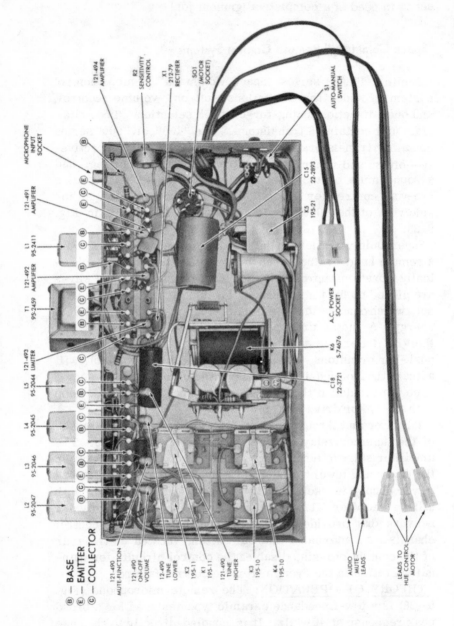

Fig. 9-23. Inside view of Zenith's S75276 remote control chassis.

200

transistor to provide degeneration for more stability. Also, the first transistor uses an emitter stabilizing resistor. The amplitude limiter, a PNP-type transistor, cuts off extraneous noise pulses and assures proper control under an extreme range of input signal strength. A 4700-ohm resistor determines the limiting point of the stage, and since it is in the collector lead it limits the peak resonant currents.

The relay driver stage operates with a -0.8 volt cutoff potential that is applied to the emitters of the four relay driver transistors, so that without signal input no DC collector current flows through the relay coils. With the -0.8 volt on the emitter, and the base at ground potential, only the negative peaks of the input sine-wave source signal will cause the transistor to conduct. (The base must become negative with respect to the emitter to cause conduction.) Thus, the transistor acts as a diode rectifier, causing relay current to flow when RF input signals are fed to its base. Note: The -0.8 voltage is the recommended factory setting. It is varied by sensitivity control potentiometer R1 and can be adjusted for the desired range of operation or sensitivity. Electrolytic capacitors are used in an integrator circuit in the relay driver collector circuits to provide a proper time constant for relay

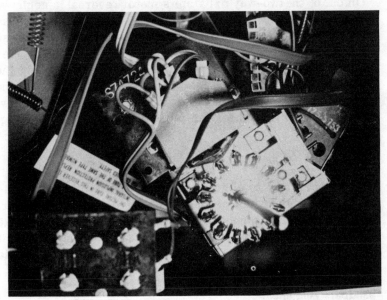

Fig. 9-24. Motor drive assembly shown mounted on the rear of a VHF tuner.

control; they also act as filters to prevent noise pulses from causing false triggering.

MOTOR DRIVE ASSEMBLY OPERATION: The switch contacts of the motor control relay, K1 and K2, in the control chassis are paralleled with the contacts of the switch located on the motor drive assembly. When the relay is energized, AC power is fed to the motor through the relay contacts. As the motor rotates, it turns the drive cam, which makes one revolution for each channel. The pin on the cam turns the large index wheel, which in turn rotates the tuner shaft. See Fig. 9-24. Also, as the drive cam rotates, it turns the rotor segment of the switch. Power supply to the motor is maintained for one or more complete drive cycles by the switch contacts. At the exact "neutral" position an index lug strikes the activating bracket assembly, moving the switch rotor segment to the "break" or off position. Or should the index lug be set to miss the activating bracket assembly the drive system will continue to cycle. Thus, by setting the index lugs tangent to the index wheel, the mechanism will skip an unwanted channel, while setting the index lug outward will cause the unit to stop on the channel. The lugs are bent or tuned for desired tripping.

On one of the two-way drive units motor reversal is achieved by the use of two windings and a series capacitor. This capacitor is switched to either motor winding to cause a phase shift, resulting in change of motor rotation. A series resistor is placed in series with the capacitor to prevent the motor drive assembly switch contacts from fusing. If the channel selector stops off index, loosen the three lock screws and reset the index wheel for proper channel stop. See Fig. 9-27.

Remote Unit Alignment

The proper way to align the remote unit is with a crystal-controlled aligner such as the Simpson Model 407. However, as most TV shops cannot invest in this type of equipment we use the next best thing—the customer's hand-controlled unit and an oscilloscope or TVOM (transistor volt/ohmmeter) to "line-up" the remote control chassis.

Bandpass Alignment

To begin aligning the "600" space command chassis, press

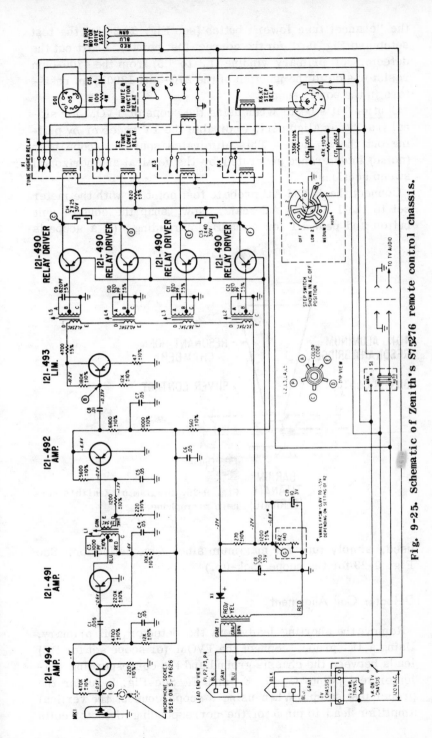

Fig. 9-25. Schematic of Zenith's S75276 remote control chassis.

the "channel tune lower" button (see Fig. 9-28 for the test setup and Fig. 9-23 for the correct test points). Short out the detector coil primary winding (L2 to L5) from the 4700-ohm resistor side to the junction of the 270- and 1200-ohm resistors in the power supply.

Caution: It's best, when using the scope or TVOM for signal tracing or alignment, to disable the TV receiver by pulling out the B+ fuse. This eliminates spurious scope hash (noise) interference generated by the vertical and horizontal sweep sections.

Connect the TVOM AC probe to test point B, with the meter set to the 1.5 volts AC scale. Now, snap the control unit button and peak L1 for a maximum reading. (If a scope is

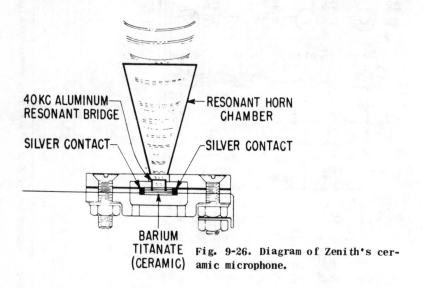

40 KC ALUMINUM RESONANT BRIDGE

RESONANT HORN CHAMBER

SILVER CONTACT

SILVER CONTACT

BARIUM TITANATE (CERAMIC)

Fig. 9-26. Diagram of Zenith's ceramic microphone.

used, simply tune for maximum sine-wave deflection. See Fig. 9-29 for the scope hook-up.)

Detector Coil Alignment

Remove the shorting lead from the detector coil primary. Using a DC probe, connect the TVOM (or scope set for DC) leads between the chassis ground and the corresponding collector test points C, D, E, and F. See Fig. 9-30 for the proper test setup. When using a scope connect the vertical amplifier lead to pin 5 of the corresponding detector coils

Fig. 9-27. Closeup view of the index wheel.

(L2, L3, L4 or L5). Snap the proper hand-control unit button and tune for maximum scope deflection; it should be about 4.5 to 5.5v p-p. Fig. 9-31 illustrates the scope display you should see.

Prior to coil alignment back out the cores of L2, L3, L4, and L5, 3/8-inch above the top of the coil forms. Now align in the following sequence: Set the TVOM to the -50-volt DC scale.

Test Point	Coil		Press hand-control unit buttons as listed below
F	(L2)	37.75 kHz	On/off volume
E	(L3)	38.75 kHz	Mute and color tint control
D	(L4)	40.25 kHz	Tune channel lower
C	(L5)	41.25 kHz	Tune channel higher

Press each hand-control button and turn the corresponding coil inward; tune each coil for a minimum reading or meter dip. Repeat the operation (two or three times) for each coil. (We begin with the lowest frequency, L5, as there is some interaction.)

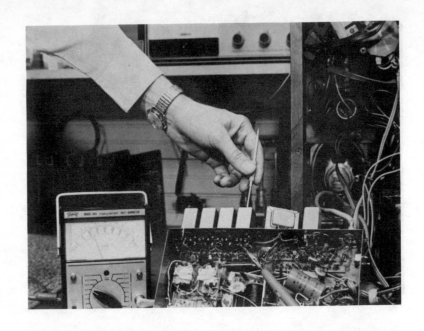

Fig. 9-28. Meter setup for relay driver alignment.

Fig. 9-29. Scope setup for bandpass alignment check.

Power Control

The automatic - manual switch (S1), located at the rear of the remote chassis, controls all power to the unit and bypasses the mute switch to assure audio even if the mute switch is locked in the sound-off position. It is set to the automatic position for remote control operation and to manual for normal operation. The auto-manual slide switch can cause trouble should it become dirty or develop loose contacts. It may cause the remote system to not operate at all or to operate intermittently. And if it is not pushed completely over to the automatic position the "tune higher channel" function may not operate. Replace or thoroughly clean and tighten the switch if these problems are encountered.

Sensitivity Control Adjustment

Bias adjustment controls sensitivity; at normal line voltage (120v AC) it should be about -0.9 volts. Under abnormal conditions, such as noisy locations, the complete set (with back on) must be at normal operating temperature before making any adjustments. Always make a final check with the customer's hand-control unit at the maximum distance it is to be used. And be sure to check all functions. Of course, where spurious noise triggering occurs, an attempt should be made to eliminate or reduce the noise before bias adjustment.

Reducing the sensitivity of the remote chassis has the effect of increasing the delay time. It may be necessary under extreme low sensitivity settings to hold down the control button for a longer time than is normal. The bandpass of the detector coils will vary directly with sensitivity. Since the bandpass narrows as sensitivity is reduced, careful alignment is vital at extremely low sensitivity settings. Since individual relay driver stage gains can vary due to coils, transistors, and relays, all functions must be checked after readjusting the sensitivity control. Do not set the sensitivity any lower than you have to. A technician is shown adjusting the sensitivity control in Fig. 9-32.

Procedure for Localizing Trouble

- Make sure the automatic-manual switch (located at the rear of the cabinet) is in the automatic position.

207

- Check the customer's hand tuning control. A loss of control signal can be caused by loose rods inside the box or broken retaining springs. Remove the four screws and take off the back cover and inspect. A loose rod can be reset with a twisting motion.
- Check or replace microphone.
- Set the auto-manual switch to the automatic position. Remove the relay dust cover and with an insulated screw-

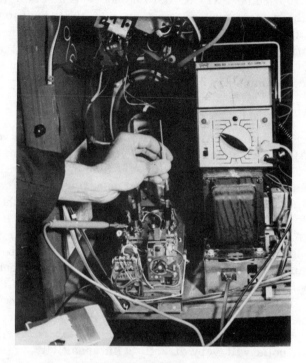

Fig. 9-30. Meter setup for detector coil
adjustment on an older chassis.

driver manually actuate each relay. If the control operates normally, the trouble is ahead of these circuits. A defective microphone, tuning control unit, or components in the control chassis may be at fault. However, if manual relay movement has no effect, the trouble is beyond that point. Check the motor drive assembly, cable assemblies, and all cable and plug connections.
- Use an oscilloscope to trace the signal from the microphone input up to the transistor driver stages. Have someone

keep pressing the hand-control button while you trace the sine-wave signal through all the amplifier stages.

- The failure of a transistor or supply voltage will result in loss of control action. Check transistors, voltages, and resistances in these circuits. If the -27-volt supply is low, filter C18 could be open or rectifier X1 is defective.
- Continuous motor rotation can be caused by a defective push-switch at the front of the receiver.

Service Tips

Poor sensitivity—all functions:

1. Weak or defective transistor.
2. Open or shorted amplifier coil L1.
3. Defective microphone.
4. Power supply. Check the voltage at X1 (should be -27v DC).

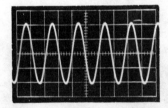

Fig. 9-31. Correct sine-wave scope display (4.5v p-p).

Poor sensitivity—one function:

1. Defective relay (check coil resistance). Check for correct mechanical action. Volume-off/on step switch may become dirty and cause loss of volume. Clean the contacts with a non-lubricant type instrument cleaner shown in Fig. 9-33. When checking relay action it is necessary for the control chassis to be in the same position as originally mounted in the receiver cabinet.
2. Control box; check the mounting of each rod and for correct hammer action. Should the remote hand unit cause the receiver remote to skip over channels where it should stop (but the channel pushbutton on the set operates OK), look for an improperly adjusted or bent damper tab. Also, a broken "spring wire," which holds the tuning rods, can cause the same channel skip problem.

Fig. 9-32. Technician shown setting sensitivity adjustment.

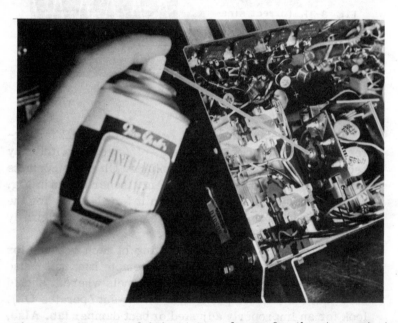

Fig. 9-33. Use a non-lubricant type cleaner for the step-contact volume control relay.

Fig. 9-34. Technician using a diamond dust burnishing tool to clean relay contacts.

3. Defective microphone; it is possible, too, for a microphone to fall off in sensitivity at some frequencies.

4. Shorted turns in a relay coil; check the resistance or try and tune the coil. The relay contacts should be cleaned with a diamond dust burnishing tool as illustrated in Fig. 9-34.

5. Many times erratic control action is caused by a ground between the microphone case and the receiver escutcheon. It's very important that this does not happen. Also, be sure the plastic grommets are in place in the microphone housing on cable-type assemblies and that the rubber gasket is in place over the front of the microphone on chassis-mounted units.

CHAPTER 10

Troubleshooting the Color Receiver

A triggered dual-trace oscilloscope really cuts down on color service time, especially when it comes to those "tough dogs." Here is a collection of "case histories."

Persistent HOT Failure

A Zenith 20X1C36 color set (see schematic Fig. 10-1) had a bad habit of burning out a 6JS6A about every week. The chassis was pulled into the shop a month before to check out this same problem, but no circuit defect could be found. So again, the 6JS6 control grid was scoped for the proper drive waveform and measured with a VTVM. It was -60 volts DC. The screen voltage checked out OK, too, and a voltage divider capacitance probe was used to check the pulse voltage at the plate of V19 (which also looked good).

Now, the scope probe was moved to the screen grid (pin 3 or 11) of V19. And what do you know, some vertical pulses were present! A couple of more scope checks in this area revealed that C123, a 40 - mfd electrolytic capacitor, had opened up. It could have been that this capacitor would intermittently short and then finally open. The resulting excessive screen current was the cause of the tube failure, apparently. With a good capacitor installed the screen grid current checked 15 ma. However, with the capacitor open the screen current rose to over 25 ma. A quick way to check current is to read the voltage drop across the 100 - ohm resistor in the screen circuit, then use Ohm's Law to determine the current flow. And don't forget, before the chassis gets off the bench, check and set the CRT anode HV to the correct level, and also check the horizontal output tube cathode current.

HOT High-Level Modulation

The preceding horizontal sweep problem brings to mind an unusual sweep trouble in an RCA color chassis—screen-grid modulation of the horizontal output tube. Fig. 10-2 is a partial schematic of the horizontal sweep stages. The picture on the screen looked a little keystoned—smaller at the bottom—but a new yoke didn't lick the problem. This called for a look at the 15.75-kHz waveform in the horizontal sweep section, with the scope set at the <u>vertical</u> scan rate. Why? Because the horizontal scan lines were shorter as the sweep went to the bottom of the CRT, so you need to see these waveforms at the vertical scan rate.

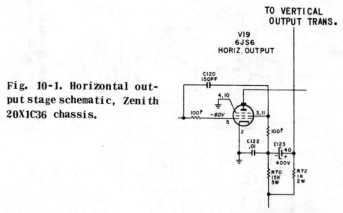

Fig. 10-1. Horizontal output stage schematic, Zenith 20X1C36 chassis.

The scope probe was connected to the grid of the horizontal output tube and the pattern was straight at the top and bottom —see Fig. 10-3 (as it should be). But what does it look like at the plate? <u>Caution</u>: There is a 5 KV pulse at the plate cap and it can damage test instruments or probes. Either use a HV capacitance divider probe or clip the scope probe onto the insulation of the plate cap lead. With the scope probe clipped to the plate cap a waveshape with an hour-glass figure appeared—see Fig. 10-4. Since the cathode is grounded, all that was left was the screen grid. The scope pattern at this point looked somewhat like a sawtooth (Fig. 10-5) voltage which was in effect modulating the sweep output tube. A few more checks revealed a defective dual section filter in the 405-volt B+ line. They are designated C118A and C118B in Fig. 10-2. Installing a new filter capacitor straightened out the problem.

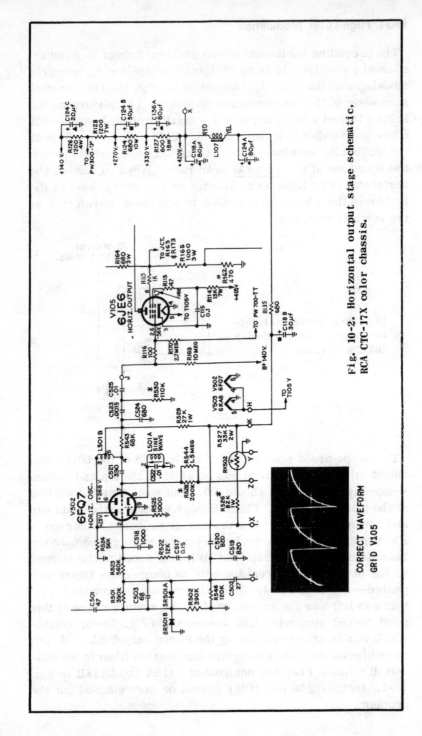

Fig. 10-2. Horizontal output stage schematic, RCA CTC-17X color chassis.

CORRECT WAVEFORM
GRID V105

214

Zenith Blanking Trouble

An electronics designer found that semiconductor devices were being destroyed in a power - supply regulating circuit. When he inspected the circuit waveforms with a limited bandwidth scope, he found no reason for the semiconductor failures. But after a little investigation with a fast rise - time wideband oscilloscope he found that brief transients of great amplitude and high energy were the cause of the destruction. Just another example of how you can put to good use that workhorse instrument.

That brings us to a case of semiconductor failure in a Zenith 20Y1C38 color chassis. Fig. 10 - 6 is the schematic of the video Y amplifier stage in question. It seems video driver TR1 and blanking diodes X2 and X3 had a very high failure rate. When transistor TR1 failed the screen went blank, and most set owners, when questioned, noticed that a crack, snap, or high-voltage arc was heard before the picture went out. This may be a good clue. In some sets the transistor was the only failure, while in other sets both diodes and the transistor would be defective. In most of these sets a HV arc apparently would occur from a pin hole in the 3A3A HV rectifier filament lead wire to the plate cap of the 3A3A or to the chassis HV cage ground. To stop this arc, new filament leads with thicker insulation should be used, plus routing the leads away from the HV cap of the HV rectifier.

But why did this HV arc take out TR1 and X2 and X3? It seems that the arc induced a high transient spike pulse into the sweep transformer blanking winding (yellow lead) which of course is coupled to blanking diode X3. On occasion the diode would short as the spike passed through to the emitter of TR1.

With transistor TR1 pulled from its socket a wideband triggered scope was connected to the TR1 socket emitter pin, and with the HV popping and arcing the high energy spike pulses appeared as shown in Fig. 10-7. Of course, the first cure is to stop the HV arc; it may be that in later production models a VDR can be installed in the emitter circuit, or some other protective device may be used. Some of these sets with diode and TR1 failure had been hit by lightning at the antenna (balun coil burnt up) which, I am sure, sent a huge transient spike all over the chassis and caused the solid-state device failures.

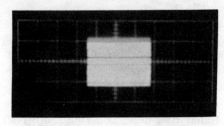

Fig. 10-3. Correct scope trace at the HOT grid (vertical rate).

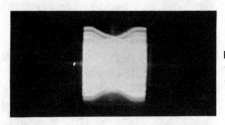

Fig. 10-4. Hour-glass wavetrace at the HOT grid (vertical rate).

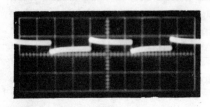

Fig. 10-5. Sawtooth voltage at the HOT screen grid (vertical rate).

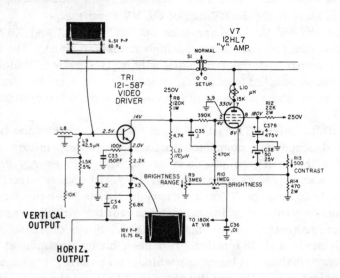

Fig. 10-6. Y amplifier schematic, Zenith 20Y1C38 chassis.

Now for a rundown of this chassis' blanking system and some problems that have cropped up. The waveshape in Fig. 10-8 shows the proper horizontal blanking information that should appear at diode X3. The diode shapes and/or cleans up the pulse (eliminating any ringing) and feeds it to the video pre-amplifier emitter (pulse amplitude is about 4.0 volts peak-to-peak). When diode X3 shorts out, the horizontal blanking pulse appears as in Fig. 10-9. Notice the ringing effect. However, the most noticeable effect is the "jail bars" pattern on the receiver screen—look at Fig. 10-10A. Whenever diode X3 or clamp diode X2 shorts or opens, it is advisable to check transistor TR1. If TR1 opens, you will see what I call "a color spoof" picture. If TR1 shorts a negative video picture results.

The wavetrace in Fig. 10-10B was observed at the CRT grid with horizontal blanking during the sync interval, driving the

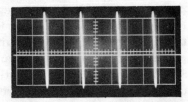

Fig. 10-7. High-energy "spikes" at the emitter terminal of TR1.

CRT to cutoff, but permitting recovery in time to start the composite information at the beginning of each scan line. Notice the composite information has a p-p amplitude of about 8 volts, and the horizontal blanking pulse does not materially exceed this amplitude even though the impressed blanking pulse on the emitter of the transistor is on the order of 4 volts. Gating clamp diode X2 (in the emitter circuit), clamps the pulse to a value which permits adequate supression, yet holds the amplitude within a range that the Y amplifier grid can accommodate.

Burst Amplifier "Spook"

The burst amplifier stage not only picks off the burst pulse but also amplifies it and delivers a burst signal on the order of 100 volts p-p to the burst amplifier plate coil—see Fig. 10-11A—where it is fed through dual capacitors to the 6JU8 diodes to develop operational DC control voltages. (See the burst amplifier circuit Fig. 10-12.) To be sure you are re-

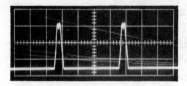

Fig. 10-8. Proper horizontal blanking pulse.

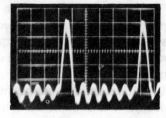

Fig. 10-9. Blanking pulse when diode X3 shorts.

ceiving color burst through the tuner and video IF amplifiers, make a scope check at the video detector. The waveform in Fig. 10-12 shows a correct color burst pulse.

It is interesting to consider that the burst amplifier tube is driven into conduction 15,750 times per second, whether or not burst is present. The fact that burst is there is merely coincident with color programming. However, the stage is pushed into conduction at regular intervals by a horizontal keying pulse as indicated in Fig. 10-11B. By using a dual-trace triggered scope the horizontal keying and color burst pulse can be checked simultaneously for correct coincident. Should no burst be present, the stage merely amplifies random circuit noise and produces a "spook" whose amplitude is on the order of 25% of the burst pulse amplitude. Since "spook" noise is the residual operating condition of the circuit, it has no influence on either color killer action or control of the 3.58-MHz oscillator. Your attention is called to the "spook" condition, however, since it takes on the appearance of "burst" if scope gain is turned up. So it's worthwhile to be aware of scope calibration in order to recognize "spook" in comparison to useful burst.

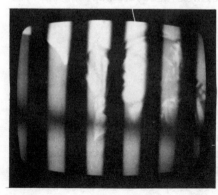

A

B

Fig. 10-10. "Jail bars" on screen of Zenith color set (A); blanking pulse at the CRT grid (8v peak-to-peak).

Burst Amplifier Checks

The use of a wideband triggered oscilloscope can be helpful in telling if all's well in various color circuits. Chroma information should appear on the plate of the first chroma amplifier...burst pulse followed by color bar information of one horizontal scan line (scope set at the horizontal rate). The 15,750 flyback keying pulse, with chroma information added, is shown in Fig. 10-13 at the burst amplifier grid. Bias on the burst amplifier grid is such that, at -40 volts, only the tip of the keying pulse (containing burst information) permits the tube to conduct. The amount of chroma displayed may depend on the sensitivity of the scope being used, though.

The "burst" pulse in Fig. 10-14A appears at the burst amplifier plate. If you experience difficulty sync'ing the scope on the narrow burst pulse, take a lead from the "external sync" binding post and dress it over the deflection yoke area to pick

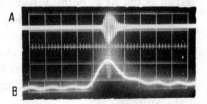

Fig. 10-11. Color burst pulse, 5X expansion (A);   horizontal burst keying pulse (B).

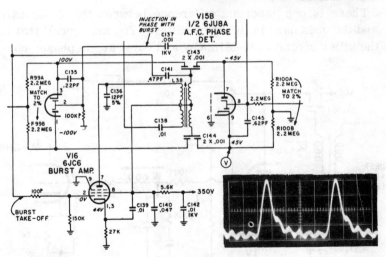

Fig. 10-12. Zenith burst amplifier circuit, with scope trace showing the color burst signal riding on the back porch of horizontal blanking pedestal.

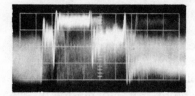

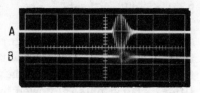

Fig. 10-13. Chroma information at the burst amplifier grid.

Fig. 10-14. Color burst signal (A); A burst spook signal (B).

off a horizontal pulse. Of course, the scope sync switch must be set to the "external" position. Fig. 10-14B is a "spook" pulse with the scope gain maintained at the same setting.

Zenith Color Oscillator AFC

Pulses from the burst amplifier plate coil are fed through two dual .001-mfd capacitors, with one side of each passing burst to the ACC color killer function of the 6JU8, as shown in Fig. 10-15. The other side of each dual capacitor passes burst to pins 7 and 9 of the 6JU8 AFC color section. Again the old faithful horizontal phase comparer action, with burst on each end of the diodes and 3.58-MHz CW inserted in the middle. The phase relationship is compared and detected as a DC voltage.

There is one important difference between this diode pair and the ones used in the color killer. You may recall that in the killer circuit 3.58-MHz CW and burst are in phase; con-

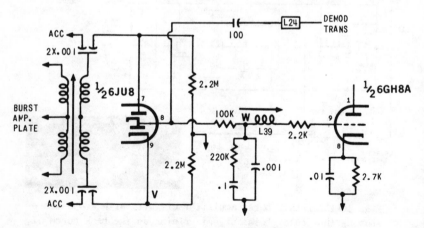

Fig. 10-15. Zenith color AFC schematic.

220

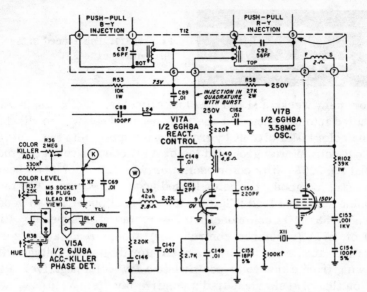

Fig. 10-16. 20XC38 Zenith color AFC schematic.

sequently, the output voltage is always one polarity—negative, and it's more or less negative depending upon the presence or absence of burst. Here, the 3.58-MHz signal is inserted in quadrature, or with a 90° phase shift of the color burst. With the 90° shift, it is now possible to create a DC voltage which can be of either polarity, plus or minus, cancelling if the oscillator is on frequency, thus achieving control of the 3.58-MHz oscillator.

DC output from the diode junction (pin 8) has a range of approximately 5 volts (test point W, Fig. 10-15), which is applied to the 3.58-MHz oscillator circuit. The voltage varies the grid bias on the reactance control triode section of the 6GH8A tube. Pin 9 of the 6JU8 is identified as test point V. It is at this point that a scope or VTVM is connected during setup of the injection transformer split (acting as a "peak detector," of maximum and minimum voltages. Please remember that the injection or demodulation transformer must feed back the correct phase and proper 3.58-MHz CW signal amplitude to the 6JU8 AFC circuit so that it will exercise proper oscillator control.

Zenith: No Color

A Zenith 23XC38 color TV chassis had poor color sync lock

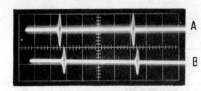

Fig. 10-17. Unbalanced 3.58-MHz burst pulses.

for many weeks and had now lost all color. The chassis was pulled into the shop and the first bench check was to disable the color killer circuit by grounding test point K in Fig. 10-16. Test point W was grounded (color AFC control voltage), too, and the 3.58-MHz color oscillator was tuned for zero beat. So far, so good: the color looked good and strong. The test point W ground lead (Fig. 10-15) was unclipped; not so good. The 3.58-MHz color oscillator went way off frequency. Pin 9 of V17A (reactance control tube) should read about zero volts, and as the 3.58-MHz oscillator drifts the voltage will swing from a few volts positive to a few volts negative. Pin 9 on this chassis measured a positive 6 volts. Well now, we must have a defective part in the AFC phase detector. And it did sound logical.

The color burst amplifier was scoped first and the wave-shapes were good (see Fig. 10-11A and 10-11B). So the color burst was checked at pins 7 and 9 of AFC phase detector V15B (Fig. 10-15). This should be a 3.58-MHz burst pulse of the same p-p amplitude. But not so in this chassis; Figs. 10-17A and B show the existing unbalanced color burst condition. All components in the AFC circuit were checked and found good. Of course, L38 could not be checked and we were quite sure it was the culprit. Also, at pin 8 of V15B you must also have a proper 3.58-MHz CW signal for phase comparison; this signal is tapped off the injection transformer. (The correct 3.58-MHz signal is shown in Fig. 10-18 with a 10X horizontal scope expansion.) The CW signal in this set was found to be low, so the color oscillator CW signal at pin 6 of V17B was scoped at 80v p-p, about 60 volts low. Just to be on the safe side, a replacement injection transformer was ordered, along with the color phase detector transformer. In this type

Fig. 10-18. 3.58-MHz CW signal at pin 8 of V15B with a 10X horizontal expansion to show detail.

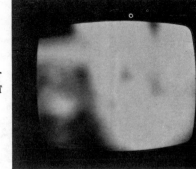

Fig. 10-19. A defocused color picture caused by an open CRT focus element.

of circuit there is good deal of inter-dependence between the two.

It so happened that the distributor had an injection trans-former in stock, but L38 was back ordered. But, in hopes it would solve the problem and cool off an impatient color set owner, the injection transformer was installed anyway. No dice; in fact, the color picture appeared worse. In a few days the replacement L38 arrived and was installed. Still no color lock and about 8 volts positive was found at pin 9 of V17A. However, the scope now displayed a balanced 3.58-MHz burst pulse at pins 7 and 9 of V15B, but the 3.58-MHz CW signal at pin 8 was almost unreadable. Could it be that the replacement injection transformer was defective? Let's install another new one. You guessed it! After a complete

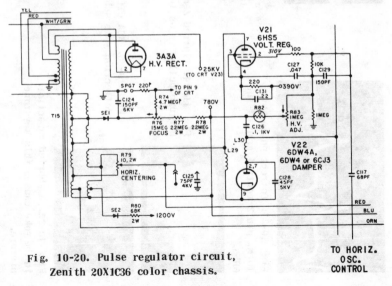

Fig. 10-20. Pulse regulator circuit, Zenith 20X1C36 color chassis.

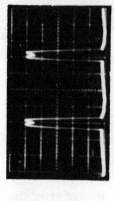

Fig. 10-23. 2000v p-p plate pulse of the 6HS5 tube. Caution: Voltage-divider probe used for this pulse check.

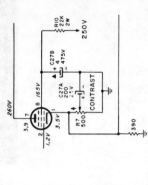

Fig. 10-27. Y amplifier schematic, Zenith 25NC37 chassis.

Fig. 10-22. Correct waveshape at cathode pin 4, pulse regulator.

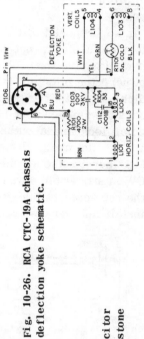

Fig. 10-26. RCA CTC-19A chassis deflection yoke schematic.

Fig. 10-21. Correct pulse waveform, pin 2 control grid of the 6HS5.

Fig. 10-24. Blurred Zenith color picture pulled in on left side.

Fig. 10-25. A shorted capacitor in the yoke caused this keystone picture.

color alignment, color was mighty fine and no voltage was present at pin 9 of V17A. Incidentally, if the 2.2 meg resistor at pin 8 of the 6JU8A AFC color phase detector is changed to 100K, you'll have stable color "lock in." This only goes to prove that new replacement parts, like new color receivers, can be defective. Oh yes, the real trouble in this chassis was a defective L38 color phase detector coil; probably leakage between coil layer windings. As you can see, new part substitution, or the old process-of-elimination method, will not always work. Your knowledge and understanding of circuit operation—plus the use of accurate professional test instruments—is what's needed in this advanced technological era.

RCA: No Focus

A very blurred, much-out-of-focus picture turned up (Fig. 10-19) on an RCA CTC-17 color chassis. At first glance this looked easy, just pop in a new 2AV2 focus rectifier. But, alas, this was just not our day. After the tubes were checked or changed, a VTVM claimed all voltages were OK at the CRT socket. The HV at the CRT anode checked out OK, too. The VTVM with the HV probe also read 4800 volts at CRT pin 9, and the focus control varied the voltage correctly through its range. The CRT socket was pulled off and pin 9 was inspected and cleaned, but it was of no help. Only one item left—the color picture tube itself. Of course, our CRT checker gave the old CRT a clean bill of health, but the only way to actually find out with this type of CRT trouble is to install a new CRT or hook the chassis up to the color test jig. A new color CRT solved the problem. Evidently, the focus element had opened up.

Zenith HV Pulse Regulator Trouble

The Zenith 20X1C36 chassis uses a 6HS5 HV regulator tube (Fig. 10-20), which is fed a flyback pulse (at control grid pin 2, Fig. 10-21) at the beginning of each horizontal sweep cycle and then "drifts" during the remainder of the cycle. The regulator's operation depends on the load present on the HV rectifier. Obviously, then, the focus voltage is always "tracking" the HV in order to improve focus during varying brightness levels. (Fig. 10-22 is the regulator cathode waveform and 10-23 is the 2000v p-p pulse found at the regulator plate.)

Now for some problems that you may encounter in this type of circuit. One chassis had sluggish HV regulation, but voltage checks in the regulator and horizontal sweep section were normal. So the scope was hooked up and the pulse regulator circuit waveshapes were checked out. At pin 2 of the HV regulator the horizontal pulse was missing. A few more checks revealed that C117, a 68-pfd capacitor from the cathode of V18B, had opened up. Result: No control pulse nor very little HV regulation. Always scope those test points!

In some Zenith color TV chassis using the 6HS5, the pulse

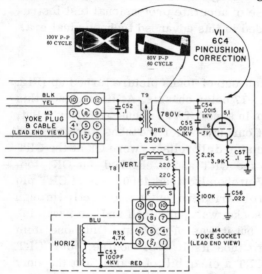

Fig. 10-28. Pincushion correction circuit, Zenith 20Y1C48 chassis.

regulator plates will run red hot and the raster will pull it on the left side (see Fig. 10-24). Then, the picture goes blurred and may black out. This usually occurs when the line voltage is 125v AC or higher. If you have this problem, replace the 6HS5 tube and remove the jumper wire from between pins 3 and 4 and ground pin 3 to the chassis. Then connect all other leads (taken off pin 3) to pin 4 (cathode) and check for correct HV setting. This same condition could be caused by an inadequate drive pulse, a gassy 3AT2, improper screen voltage, shorted yoke or sweep transformer, and other excessive loads on the sweep circuits. However, you should make this modification first.

Keystoned Raster

Since the days of B/W a keystone-shaped picture casts the

226

shadow of suspicion on shorted yoke windings or a shorted capacitor across the deflection coils. Fig. 10-25 shows a color keystone picture taken from the screen of an RCA CTC-19A color chassis (see the schematic in Fig. 10-26). In this case, it wasn't the yoke; it was a shorted 100-pfd 3KV capacitor across the horizontal deflection yoke winding, L102.

Not only can a shorted horizontal coil winding cause this same problem but shorts between the vertical and horizontal coil will, too. Many times the yoke, or the capacitors in the yoke circuit, will cause a loss of high voltage and of course the CRT screen will not light up. If the horizontal sweep circuits check out OK and the CRT and associated circuits are all right, the horizontal yoke is a good suspect. To determine if the deflection yoke is defective, substitute a variable inductance (a coil that can be adjusted from 10 to 50 millihenries) in place of the horizontal yoke windings. If you don't have a variable inductance or a substitute yoke, the following method will get the job done: Slip the yoke off the CRT and turn on the set from a cold start. Place the yoke away from the tubes in the set so they won't heat it up. Let the receiver operate about 15 minutes, then—after turning

Fig. 10-29. White streaks across the screen caused by an open B+ filter capacitor.

off the set—carefully feel around all of the yoke windings. If you detect a warm winding or hot spot, the yoke has a shorted winding and is defective. This method works for a check of the vertical yoke windings, too. Also, carefully touch any capacitors on the yoke; if any are hot or warm, replace them too.

Incorrect Contrast Control Operation

The customer's complaint on a Zenith 25NC37 color TV chassis said, "The contrast control thinks it's a brightness control!" As it turned out he wasn't too far from right! In fact, the picture on this set would bloom, and then when the contrast control was turned up—fully clockwise—the screen would go dark. This symptom is quite confusing and may seem impossible. However, it can happen and the "bad actor" in this set was a shorted 200-mfd electrolytic capacitor (C27A in Fig. 10-27) in the contrast control circuit. The capacitor is the Y amplifier cathode bypass, connecting from the center leg of the contrast control to chassis ground.

Should the capacitor open the symptom would be no contrast control action at all, or if the capacitor is partially open, the

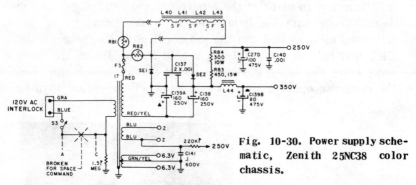

Fig. 10-30. Power supply schematic, Zenith 25NC38 color chassis.

contrast control would have only partial effect. Some color sets have been known to produce a varying amount of picture contrast level. C27A will cause this trouble, too, if it has become intermittently defective. Of course, if the contrast control (R7, Fig. 10-27) is bad, it will cause the troubles just mentioned.

Oscillation in a Pincushion Correction Circuit

This problem caused quite a "flap" in the shop until it was solved. At top left corner of the screen a "colored ball" appeared, but on another set it took the form of an eagle at the bottom of the screen. These "happenings" were found in a Zenith color TV chassis using a 6KT8 tube for pincushion correction.

After much time and effort, some strange oscillations were

found at the 6KT8 plate pin 3 and control grid pin 2 (V11A in Fig. 10-28). It seems the oscillation developed as a result of some component tolerance variations. Our cure for this problem is to install ferrite sleeves over all leads connected to the pincushion correction circuits of V11A. This will then dampen any oscillation that may appear.

"White Streaks"

This trouble has been found in both Zenith B/W and color TV sets, plus other makes of receivers. Fig. 10-29 is a picture of what you may see. At times, when you first turn the set on the streaks will appear and then the picture goes black. Many times this symptom will be accompanied by a loud high-pitched squeal emitting from the horizontal sweep system.

As you may have already guessed the problem is caused by an open filter capacitor in the B+ supply. The filter that caused this trouble in a Zenith 25NC38 chassis (Fig. 10-30) is C27D, the filter capacitor in the 250-volt B+ line that supplies voltage to the horizontal oscillator and sweep circuits. Bridge a new capacitor across the 250-volt line or use a scope to check for above normal AC ripple.

CHAPTER 11

Scoping the Electronic
Power Supply

If a power supply furnishes incorrect voltage—too high or too low—if it is not rectifying properly, if the output contains too much AC ripple or transient spikes, the electronic device it supplies just cannot function properly. Now, what can go wrong with the power supply and how can it affect circuit operation? Let's see how the power supply operates and what methods can be used to check it out.

Basic Power Supply Tests

To set the stage, let's review a few basic power supply circuits. Fig. 11-1 is a simple half-wave circuit with a minimum of three filter capacitors. Some TV receivers may use eight or nine such filter capacitors.

Power supply filters are usually of the low-pass LC variety, with the cut-off frequency as far below the ripple voltage as is feasible. Generally two types of filters are used. The first, called an inductive-input filter, has a series inductor immediately after the rectifier. The second is the capacitive-input filter, which has a shunt capacitor right after the rectifier. One or more filter sections may be used. Fig. 11-2 shows a two-section inductive-input filter, while the circuit in Fig. 11-3 is a two-section capacitive-input filter circuit. An inductive-input filter provides a lower output voltage but offers better voltage regulation than a capacitive-input filter. The capacitive-input filter also produces a much higher peak current in the rectifiers. Obviously, an oscilloscope will help locate filter capacitor defects faster and easier.

One electrolytic defect is AC leakage between multiple sections. This stray signal can be introduced into receiver stages from other sections of the chassis. The scope is the only way to detect this type defect. The old "hunt-and-try" method of shunting a suspected filter with a good capacitor will not reveal this type of problem. Current leakage through the cover of paper-encased filters is also another problem.

Some Power Supply Circuits

The simple half-wave doubler power supply in Fig. 11-4 is found in many modern TV receivers. The filter capacitors and the choke, or resistor preceding each capacitor, are considered as primary filter circuits. C1 refines the pulsating DC (at the rectifier output) into a steady DC voltage having a ripple of not more than 10%. C2 (with choke or resistor preceding it) reduces the ripple, producing a smoother DC with a semi-sine-wave ripple around 2%. Also, C2 bypasses stray

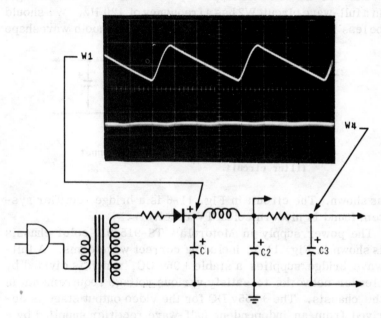

Fig. 11-1. Simple half-wave power supply circuit.

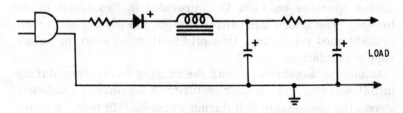

Fig. 11-2. Two-section inductive-input filter circuit.

signals picked up along the supply line, preventing undesired inter-stage coupling. C3 smoothes the DC further, also providing increased decoupling between stages and a ground return for all signals on the line.

Illustrated in Fig. 11-5 is a full-wave voltage doubler circuit; here, C5 functions quite differently, as it is not a filtering capacitor. Operating with D1, C5 charges to the peak value of the applied AC voltage. Using this DC charge as a reference, the second rectifier D2 produces a DC voltage approximately equal to the peak-to-peak value of the AC supply voltage. Hence, the DC obtained is approximately two times the RMS value of the supplied AC voltage.

Normal oscilloscope waveforms are shown in these circuits. W1 is a 60-Hz sawtooth ripple equal to 10% of the DC voltage. In a full-wave circuit W2 has a frequency of 120 Hz. W4 should be less than one-volt amplitude and have a smooth waveshape

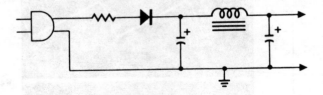

Fig. 11-3. Two-section capacitive-input filter circuit.

as shown. The circuit in Fig. 11-6 is a bridge rectifier system found in modern color TV receivers.

The power supply in Motorola's TS-915/919 color chassis is shown in Fig. 11-7, including correct waveforms. A full-wave bridge supplies a stable +95v DC, which is divided by bleeder networks to satisfy various voltage requirements in the chassis. The +255v DC for the video output stage is derived from an independent half-wave rectifier supplied by a separate winding on the power transformer. Most of the receiver operates on +35v DC, provided by two diodes in the bridge. The choke input filter system and the bridge circuit provide good regulation, thus eliminating any need for power supply regulation.

Automatic degaussing, with decreasing correction during initial warmup, is another feature. A thermistor gradually shorts the degaussing coil during warm-up. In turn, a heat-sensitive bi-metal switch shorts both. Warm-up time is quite

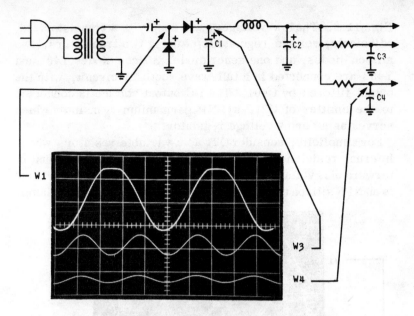

Fig. 11-4. Half-wave doubler circuit.

fast—about 7 seconds. A conventional circuit breaker and RF filters are evident in the primary circuit. The total power input for this chassis varies from 125 to 200 watts, depending upon CRT brightness setting. Another bridge-type power supply circuit is shown in Fig. 11-8; it is used in Zenith's 20Y1C48 color TV chassis.

Transistorized Regulated Power Supply

The zener diode's characteristics make it desirable for use as a constant voltage reference for power supply regulation, taking the place of the gas VR (voltage regulator tube). The zener diode exhibits a sharp break in its reverse I-E characteristic at some pre-determined voltage, due to avalanche breakdown, and the breakdown characteristic is such that a wide range of currents can be passed while the voltage across the device remains essentially constant. The action of the zener also serves to filter out the ripple voltage in the supply current, thus fewer filter capacitors are needed.

Let's look at how an actual transistor regulated power supply works in a TV receiver. A General Electric portable TA chassis power supply will illustrate the pertinent points. See

233

Fig. 11-9. The low-voltage power supply is a transistorized, adjustable, voltage-regulated type using two transistors, two silicon diodes, and one zener diode. Silicon diodes Y401 and Y402 are connected in a full-wave rectifier circuit, with the output filtered by C401. The DC output voltage is connected to the emitter of Q21, a PNP germanium transistor which serves as a series voltage regulator.

For simplicity, consider Q21 as a variable resistor, whose internal resistance can be varied by changing the amount of forward bias voltage applied to the emitter-base junction. Q20 is an NPN silicon transistor which functions as an error amp-

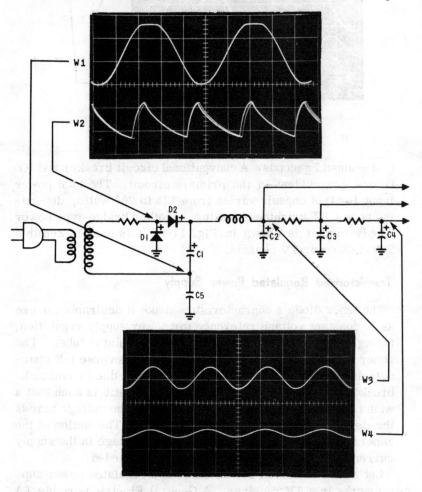

Fig. 11-5. Full-wave doubler circuit.

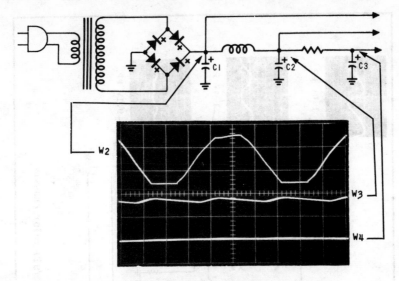

Fig. 11-6. Bridge rectifier circuit.

lifier capable of responding to voltage variations which appear at the collector of Q21 and adjusting the base bias on Q21 to keep the output voltage at a constant amplitude. The base voltage on Q20 is supplied from the series voltage divider—R405, R406, R407, and the regulator voltage adjustment control. The cathode of the zener diode Y403 is connected to the collector of Q21, which is the output of the DC supply. Its anode is connected in series with R403 to chassis ground. The emitter of Q20 is connected at the junction of R403 and Y403. A constant reference voltage equal to 6.3 volts DC is developed across Y401 through zener diode action. The emitter voltage on Q20 will always be equal to the difference between 6.3 volts DC and the collector voltage at Q21.

If the AC line voltage rises, the output voltage at Y401 and Y402 and the collector voltage of Q21 will rise. Consequently, the base voltage of Q20 will go more positive, but by a smaller amount in comparison to its emitter-voltage rise, effectively decreasing the amount of forward bias applied across its emitter-base junction. This voltage change lowers the emitter-collector current of Q20, which is flowing through the emitter-base junction of Q21. The effect of this change decreases the amount of forward bias applied to the emitter-base junction of Q21 and the transistor will not conduct as heavily. The internal resistance of Q21 will rise and the voltage drop across

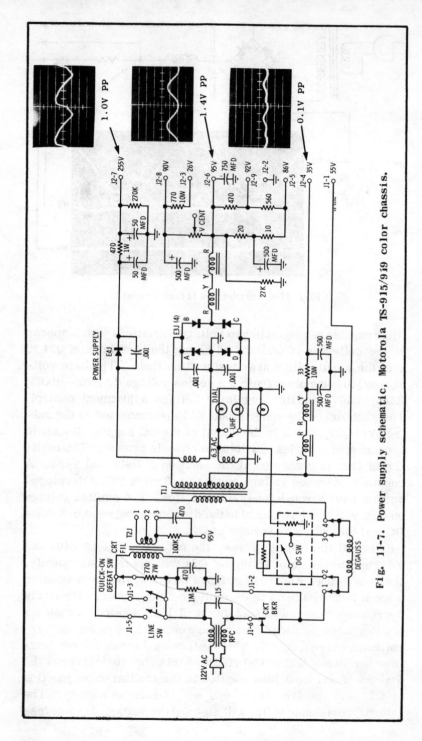

Fig. 11-7. Power supply schematic, Motorola TS-915/919 color chassis.

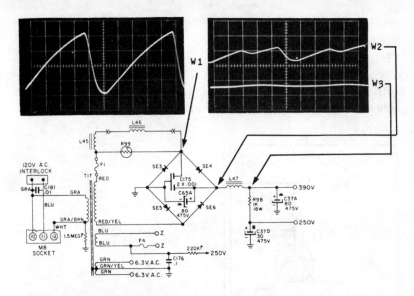

Fig. 11-8. Power supply schematic, Zenith 20Y1C48 color chassis.

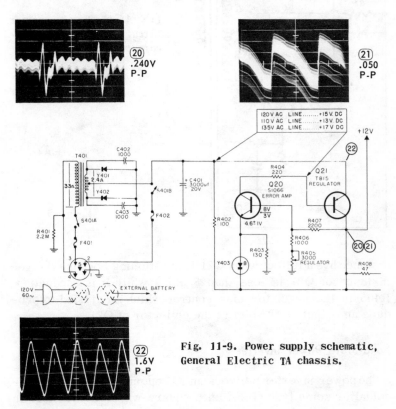

Fig. 11-9. Power supply schematic, General Electric TA chassis.

it will be higher, thus lowering the power supply output voltage to its original 12 volts.

R402 assures that the regulator circuit starts to function when power is applied to the receiver by supplying an initial voltage to the base of error amplifier Q20. Since R402 is connected between the emitter and collector of Q21, its re-

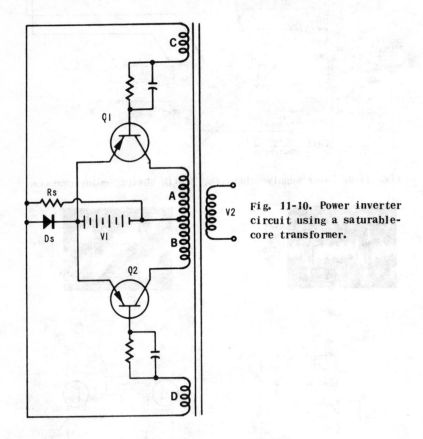

Fig. 11-10. Power inverter circuit using a saturable-core transformer.

sistance has no effect when Q21 is functioning because the resistance of Q21 is less than 8 ohms while it is conducting. R405 is the regulator bias control which is adjusted to produce an output of 12 volts at the collector of Q21.

Solid-State Power Inverter

The power inverter delivers an AC output that may be sinusoidal or some type of switched square-wave. Somewhere in

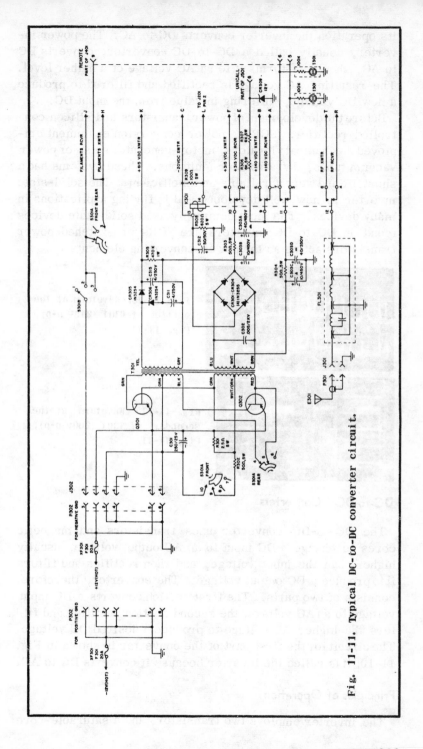

Fig. 11-11. Typical DC-to-DC converter circuit.

its operation the inverter converts DC to AC. The power inverter, usually called a DC-to-DC converter, converts DC to AC, then transforms it to an AC voltage of a higher level. The resulting AC voltage is rectified and filtered to produce a new DC voltage, differing in value from the input DC.

Before the development of power transistors and silicon controlled rectifiers (SCRs), power conversion equipment employed mechanical vibrators, motor-generator sets, or power vacuum tubes, thyratrons or ignitrons. These systems had a short life and were unreliable and inefficient. The solid-state inverter is now well developed and is finding applications in many devices. The most commonly used solid-state devices found in DC-to-DC inverters are SCRs or switched power transistors acting as the power-converting elements.

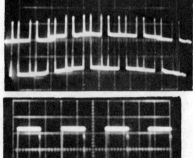

Fig. 11-12. Waveform at the emitter of Q301 (215v p-p), Fig. 11-11.

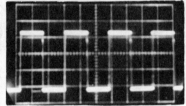

Fig. 11-13. Waveform at the secondary of T301 (200v p-p), Fig. 11-11.

DC-to-DC Converters

The DC-to-DC converter uses transistors and magnetic cores to change a DC input to an AC output voltage, usually higher than the input voltage, and then rectifies and filters it to produce a DC output voltage. The converter, therefore, consists of two parts. The first section converts a DC input voltage to an AC voltage; the second section rectifies and filters the higher AC voltage to produce a desired DC voltage. The circuit for the first part of the converter is shown in Fig. 11-10; it is called the inverter because it converts DC to AC.

Principles of Operation

The inverter employs two transistors and a saturable-core

240

transformer of "square-loop" material. The desirable feature of the square-loop material is that it exhibits a sharp saturation characteristic. In the operation of the circuit in Fig. 11-10, the transistors are used as on-off switches. For the PNP transistors shown, a negative base-to-emitter voltage of sufficient magnitude will cause the transistor to be "on" or conducting, and there will be only a small resistance, called the saturation resistance, between the transistor collector and emitter. A zero or positive base-to-emitter current will cause the transistors to be "off" and there will be a very high resistance between its collector and emitter.

If, for example, transistor Q1 is on or conducting and transistor Q2 is cut off or not conducting, a slowly rising current will flow in winding A until the core saturates. During this time there are induced voltages in windings B, C, D, and the the output winding. The voltage induced in winding C keeps transistor Q1 saturated and the voltage induced in winding D

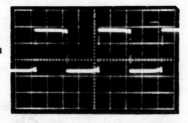

Fig. 11-14. Waveform at T301 with the circuit loaded, Fig. 11-11.

keeps transistor Q2 cut off. The voltage induced across winding B adds to the supply voltage, causing a voltage to appear at the collector of Q2. Once begun, the process of driving the core to positive and negative saturation around the transformer loop is self-sustaining. Diode Ds and the resistor Rs (Fig. 11-10) form a "starting circuit" to bias the transistors into the active state and insure that oscillations are started.

At starting time, diode Ds is reverse biased and the transistors are forward biased through resistor Rs. The voltage drop across Ds is low and equal to the drop across the emitter junction and the base resistors. After oscillations begin, the voltages developed by feedback windings C and D are high enough to maintain forward bias across Ds. A forward-biased diode offers a low resistance; therefore, Ds effectively shunts Rs out of the circuit. The capacitors and resistors in the transistor base circuits are chosen to improve the transient switching time and to limit the transistor base currents.

DC-to-DC converters are put to work in many ways. They are used in mobile 2-way radios, tape recorders, radio receivers, and mobile public address amplifiers.

The typical DC-to-DC power supply converter, shown in Fig. 11-11, is used in a 50-watt Aerotron mobile transceiver. The scope trace in Fig. 11-12 was taken at the emitter of Q301. The waveform in Fig. 11-13 appears at the secondary of transformer T301. Fig. 11-14 was observed at the same test point but the output pulse width is increased because the converter is being loaded during transmission.

De-Spiking Network

As it turns off, spikes often appear across the collector-to-emitter junction of a switching transistor, as shown in Fig.

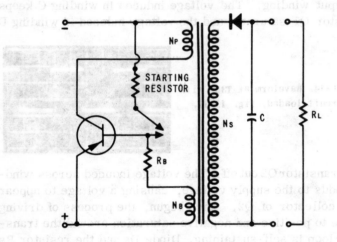

Fig. 11-16. "Ringing choke" converter circuit.

11-15. This spike may exceed the transistor voltage rating and should be kept to a minimum. These spikes are generated in the circuit, or by the load, and are not spikes appearing on the converter power source. One of the most common source of spikes is the converter transformer. A small value of capacitance can be placed across the primary, as shown as C301 in Fig. 11-11. This gives a storage device which absorbs the energy released when the transformer flux collapses during switching.

One of the greatest causes of power converter failure is the presence of spikes or excessive ripple on the input supply. These spikes can be of very short duration and might not be seen on a service scope, but they can exceed the breakdown voltage of the oscillator transistors. This is very true when a battery that energizes the converter also supplies motor loads, or is charged by a generator with a slow response regulator. Also, it's likely to happen on converter power sources that are rectified from the AC power system. Slow response systems, such as magnetic amplifier regulated supplies, can cause high line spikes. To check for these spikes a fast triggered scope is a must.

Ringing Choke Converter

Another transistor-magnetic converter is the ringing choke

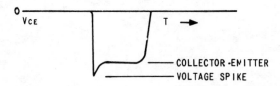

Fig. 11-15. Spike which may appear at the collector-to-emitter junction as a transistor switches off.

converter shown in Fig. 11-16. The circuit looks like a blocking oscillator or one-half of a DC-to-DC converter. One difference between the ringing choke converter and the DC-to-DC converter is that no power transfer to the load occurs in the ringing choke converter while the transistor is on. The case is the opposite for the DC-to-DC converter. Load energy is stored in the magnetic field of the core. When the transistor in Fig. 11-16 is saturated, almost full input voltage is applied to the transformer primary. Under this condition, a linearly-rising current flows in the collector circuit. Feedback is applied by means of the base winding which generates a constant voltage determined by the input voltage and the turns ratio.

The disadvantages of the ringing choke converter are the limited amount of energy per cycle which can be stored in a core of a given size and the poor voltage regulation. This converter is, however, a simple device for developing high voltages at low currents. The efficiency can be as high as 85% for one or two watts of power output.

GLOSSARY

ACCELERATING POTENTIAL: The voltage difference between cathode and anode in a CRT, used for accelerating the electron beam.

AMPLITUDE LINEARITY: The proportionality of the electron-beam displacement to the signal voltage.

ATTENUATORS: Devices for reducing the input voltage, usually by a fixed ratio.

BANDWIDTH: The upper and lower limits where the amplitude response of an amplifier (to a sinusoidal waveform) becomes 0.707 (-3 db) the amplitude of a reference frequency. When only one number appears, it is taken on the upper limit.

BALANCED INPUT: A differential input where each side of the circuit has the same series resistance.

BEAM BLANKING: Causing the electron beam to disappear by application of a pulse to the CRT control grid or cathode.

BLANKING TIME: The length of time the electron beam is shut off.

BLANKING VOLTAGE: The voltage applied to the CRT grid or cathode to blank out the electron beam.

CALIBRATED TRIGGERED SWEEP: A sweep occurring only when initiated by a pulse and moving horizontally at a known rate such as 1 microsecond or 1 second per centimeter.

CHOPPED IMPULSE WAVE: An impulse that is cut off in midwave.

CHOPPED MODE: A time-sharing method of displaying output signals of two or more channels with a single CRT gun, in sequence, at a rate not referenced to the sweep.

CHOPPING RATE: The rate at which channel switching occurs in the Chopped Mode.

CLAMPING CIRCUIT: A circuit that holds one extreme (maximum or minimum) of an input signal at a fixed voltage.

COMMON-MODE REJECTION (COMMON-SIGNAL REJECTION): The balancing out of input noise in a differential input.

CURRENT PROBE: A transformer type probe used for measuring the current in a conductor, usually by means of a snap-around (inductive-coupling) configuration.

DEFLECTION FACTOR: The distance a CRT electron beam moves for a given change of potential. It is normally expressed as volts per centimeter.

DELAYED SWEEP: A feature whereby the sweep is initiated at a fixed time after a predetermined signal.

DIFFERENTIAL INPUT: A dual input where two independent waveforms are added to or subtracted, producing a single input signal.

DIFFERENTIAL SIGNAL: The instantaneous, algebraic difference between two signals.

DOUBLE-MODING: Frequency jumping; i.e., changing abruptly from one frequency to another at irregular intervals.

DUTY CYCLE: Ratio of pulse width to pulse-repetition time.

FALL TIME (DECAY TIME): The length of time necessary for the amplitude of a pulse to decrease from 90% to 10% of its maximum.

FLUORESCENCE: Emission of light from a substance (a phosphor) during excitation by radiant energy.

FREE-RUNNING, OR RECURRENT, SWEEP: A continuous movement of the electron beam across the CRT face at the horizontal-sweep generator frequency.

GATE PULSE: An applied voltage that causes a circuit to operate only while the voltage is present.

GRASS: Alternate term for noise voltages.

HARMONIC (HARMONIC FREQUENCY): A multiple of the fundamental frequency.

HYSTERESIS: A lag of magnetic flux with respect to the applied magnetizing force.

INPUT RC CHARACTERISTICS: The DC resistance and capacitance to ground present at the input of an oscilloscope.

INTENSITY MODULATION: The process and/or effect of varying the electron beam current in a cathode-ray tube resulting in varying brightness or luminance of the trace.

INTERNAL CALIBRATOR: An internal source of square-wave voltage, used for calibrating a cathode-ray oscilloscope.

INTERNAL GRATICULE: A graticule whose rulings are a permanent part of the inner surface of the cathode-ray tube faceplate.

INTERNAL TRIGGERING: The use of a portion of a deflection signal (usually the vertical deflection signal) as a triggering signal source.

JITTER: Instability of a CRT display.

LISSAJOUS FIGURES: Patterns obtained on a scope screen by applying sine-wave voltages to the horizontal and vertical inputs (used to determine relative frequency).

LUMINANCE: The photometric equivalent of brightness.

MAGNIFIED SWEEP: A sweep whose time per division has been decreased by amplification of the sweep waveform rather than by changing the time constants used to generate it.

MEGACYCLE (MEGAHERTZ): One million cycles.

MICROSECOND: One-millionth of a second.

MILLIMICROSECOND: One-thousandth of one-millionth of a second.

MODE: The manner in which the scope controls are set up.

NANOSECOND: Same as millimicrosecond. A thousandth of a microsecond, or a billionth of a second.

NONLINEAR: Descriptive term applied to an output when its amplitude is not directly proportionate to that of the input signal.

OVERSHOOT: The initial height to which a pulse rises above the general level of its top.

PARALLAX: The apparent displacement of an observed object due to the angle of observation.

PARAPHASE AMPLIFIER: An electronic configuration which converts a single-ended input to a double-ended output.

PASSBAND: The width of a frequency spectrum, in cycles per second, that is accepted and amplified by a circuit.

PEAKING TRANSFORMER: A transformer in which the core saturates early in each cycle, causing the secondary to produce a sharp voltage peak.

PERSISTENCE: See phosphor Decay.

PHASE: A quantity that specifies the relative position of a wave with respect to a specific point in time.

PHASE LOCK: The synchronization of the local oscillator with a stable reference frequency.

PHASE SHIFT: A shift in the position of a wave with respect to a reference point.

PHOSPHOR: The material on the inside face of the cathode-ray tube that glows when struck by an electron beam.

PHOSPHOR DECAY: A phosphorescence curve, energy emitted versus time.

PHOSPHORESCENCE: Emission of light from a substance after excitation has been removed.

POWER FACTOR: The ratio of watts to volt-amperes, or actual power to apparent power. It is equal to the cosine of the phase angle between current and voltage waveforms when both are sinusoidal.

PRF: Abbreviation for pulse-recurrence frequency.

PULSE: A short, sudden change of voltage or current.

PULSE-FORMING LINE: A combination of inductors and capacitors used for generating a square pulse of given duration.

PULSE POWER: The energy content of a pulse, expressed as either an average or a peak value.

PULSE SAMPLING: A method whereby samples are taken from successive pulses in order to reduce a very high-frequency wave.

PULSE WIDTH: The duration of a pulse measured at the 50% amplitude points.

Q: Quality factor, or figure of merit. The ratio, at resonance, of reactance to resistance.

REAL-TIME SAMPLING: A sampling process in which more than one sample is taken for each signal event. The time required for display construction is the same as the time represented in the display.

RECEIVER GATING: Application of pulses for electronically switching a receiver off and on.

RECOVERY TIME: (1) Of a receiver, the time required for it to resume half its full sensitivity after a pulse has been transmitted. (2) Of a TR switch, the time required after gap ionization for a received signal to rise to half its full amplitude.

REPETITION RATE: Rate of occurrence of successive pulses, expressed in cycles per second (pulses per second).

RESOLUTION (CATHODE-RAY TUBE): A measure of the total number of trace lines discernible along the coodinate axes, bounded by the extremities of the graticule or other specific limits.

RF: Abbreviation for radio frequency.

RINGING: A damped-wave oscillation generated from shock excitation of an LCR circuit.

RISE TIME: The length of time necessary for the amplitude of a pulse to increase from 10% to 90% of maximum.

ROLLOFF: A gradually increasing loss or attenuation with increase or decrease of frequency beyond the substantially flat portion of the amplitude-frequency response characteristic.

ROUNDING: In the display of a step function (usually of time), the loss of the corner following the step.

SIGNAL DELAY: A delay built into the signal circuit of a scope. It permits the horizontal sweep to start early in order to display the whole pulse.

SPECTRUM ANALYZER: A test instrument that displays the distribution of energy contained in the frequencies emitted by a pulsed magnetron. It is also used for general testing of system characteristics.

STORAGE OSCILLOSCOPE: An instrument that retains the image of a pulse for an extended period—for days, if necessary.

SWEEP DELAY: The delay before the sweep is triggered.

SWEEP MAGNIFIER: A device that expands the sweep range. A 5x magnifier will change 1 microsecond per centimeter to 0.2 microsecond per centimeter.

SWEEP RANGE: The range of sweep speed, such as 1 microsecond per centimeter to 5 seconds per centimeter.

SYNCHRONIZE: To adjust two waves or pulses so they occur at the same time (in phase).

SYNCHROSCOPE: An oscilloscope utilizing a triggered, calibrated sweep to display either recurrent or nonrepetitive pulses. Refinements such as delay lines, magnifiers, differential-input amplifiers, and trigger-level facilities are also commonly provided.

TIME-BASE GENERATOR: Same as the scope horizontal sweep multivibrator generator.

TIME-MARK GENERATOR: A circuit that produces pulses at accurate intervals for display on the oscilloscope screen.

TRIGGER POINT: The point on the input pulse where the sweep is triggered.

TRIGGER PULSE: A pulse which starts a cycle of operation.

UNBLANKING GENERATOR: A circuit producing a pulse that turns on the CRT trace.

VERTICAL-FREQUENCY RESPONSE: The bank of frequencies passed by the vertical amplifiers.

VERTICAL AMPLIFICATION: The signal gain in the vertical-amplifying circuits of the oscilloscope.

WRITING SPEED: The rate at which a line is traced on a scope screen or photographic film. It is usually expressed in inches per microsecond.

ZERO-TIME REFERENCE: A reference point in time from which the action of all circuits in a radar system are measured.

Index